IE AND ITS MEASUREMENT

PHOTO BY GUSTAV WEISSNER

For more than twenty years, Harrison J. Cowan has been associated with the watchmaking industry. As Director of Public Relations for the Longines-Wittnauer Watch Company, he has worked closely with astronomers, scientists, and researchers in this field. Mr. Cowan has also been active in directing and timing sports events of all kinds—the auto races on the Bonneville Salt Flats in Utah, and the World Ski Championships in Maine and Colorado, for example. He is presently organizing the complex system of electrical timing for the VIII Winter Olympic Games to be held in California in 1960. The first outline of *Time and Its Measurement* was created as a guide to an exhibit on the history of time and time-keeping for the Hayden Planetarium in New York City.

Time an

CLEVELAND AND NEW YORK

Harrison J. Cowan

ts Measurement

FROM THE STONE AGE TO THE NUCLEAR AGE

THE WORLD PUBLISHING COMPANY

PUBLISHED BY The World Publishing Company

2231 WEST 110TH STREET, CLEVELAND 2, OHIO

PUBLISHED SIMULTANEOUSLY IN CANADA BY

NELSON, FOSTER & SCOTT LTD.

Contents

LIST OF ILLUSTRATIONS

Foreword

THE NEED TO RECORD and interrelate units of time has always confronted man. From the earliest times, when he apportioned the habits of his existence according to the day and the night and the warmth and the cold, better and more accurate means of establishing intervals have been required. The story of the development of such devices, from the gnomon and the water clock through the modern watch and clock in all their refinement—and even further into the theory of time—this is the task that has been undertaken by the author of this book. It is a welcome effort, for most such work of the past has been either quite technical or aimed exclusively at the youngsters. Here the story is related competently yet entertainingly for a mature audience.

The author has been intimately associated with the watchmaking industry for many years. He has been involved in the solution of many curious and difficult timekeeping problems. He has helped, for example, to improve the accuracy of methods used in clocking sports events. He knows the problems of manufacturing, the parts that comprise a modern watch, and the evolution of the arts and crafts involved. All of these elements of experience are woven into the text.

I am certain that the reader will more greatly appreciate his own wrist or pocket watch, and will have a better understanding of the elusive subject of time as a result of reading this book.

JOSEPH MILES CHAMBERLAIN
Director, American Museum—
Hayden Planetarium

New York City
Spring, 1958

ACKNOWLEDGMENTS

MUCH of the information in this volume was acquired during a period of twenty active years in the watch industry. Since it was my job to write about time, I set about trying to learn something about it—from books and periodicals, from associates and technicians, from watch and clock collectors, and from astronomers and scientists as well.

In any history there are many opinions, and in timekeeping, even some modern conceptions are subjects for stormy debate. I have tried to be as factual as possible, and have presented a highly condensed story in some chronological arrangement, with a minimum of natural and human bias and prejudice.

In the astronomical subject matter, with which I had meager acquaintance, I am grateful for the assistance of Joseph M. Chamberlain, Thomas D. Nicholson, and members of the staff of the Hayden Planetarium of New York, for much patient and tolerant counsel. I am glad to acknowledge the assistance of Henry B. Fried, an authority on watches, for checking the manuscript for technical content, and for permission to reproduce his drawings of modern escapements, including the series on the action of the detached lever escapement. I would like to thank Dr. G. M. Clemence, Director of the Nautical Almanac of the United States Naval Observatory, for permission to quote from his scientific papers. To the many others who answered questions and offered advice and suggestions, thank you one and all.

The three-dimensional drawings which clarify the astronomical chapters in the book were especially drawn for this volume by Helmut Wimmer.

My hope is that this book will help toward an understanding and appreciation of the rhythm of the universe which we call time, and man's efforts over the centuries to live within it.

TIME AND ITS MEASUREMENT

CHAPTER I

The Dawn of Time

Reconstructing History

HOW MANY MILLIONS of years man may have lived on this earth is a question still unanswered. Four times, geologists tell us, glaciers flowed down from the polar icecap. As they melted and receded, they flooded vast areas. The periods of time were enormous. It has been calculated that it required five thousand years for the ice mass to recede from the southern to the northern boundary of New York State. The story of Noah and the flood has its duplicate in the folklore of many peoples, and might well have occurred at the end of the last ice age. Modern anthropologists believe that men, walking erect and with some developed culture, lived on earth a million years ago.

Evidence of ancient history of man is most fragmentary. There is no continuity in the record prior to about five thousand years before the Christian Era. Most important to the student of time is the fact that much of what we know of the ancient past was unearthed in comparatively recent years. We can deduce that the people of the city of Ur, in Mesopotamia, had a high degree of culture. From this city Abraham is supposed to have set out for another country, and became the father of the Hebrews. From this same region, it is believed, others set out to plant the seeds of civilization in India and China.

The astronomical knowledge and timekeeping system of ancient Mesopotamia is just now being slowly deciphered from clay tablets which archaeologists have unearthed. Around 3000 B.C., the Sumerians, who built the Biblical Tower of Babel, had a method of writing on soft clay tablets with a wedge-shaped stylus, with characters which we now call cuneiform. From this evidence we have found that the people had a calendar and a week of 7 days. They divided the whole day of 24 hours into 12 periods. Each of these divisions was equal to 2 of our hours. They divided these periods into 30 parts. One of these parts was equal to 4 minutes, as we count time today.

But this knowledge was soon lost to the world. The culture of the Sumerians of ancient Mesopotamia rose and fell, as did the cultures of Babylonia, Assyria, Chaldea, Persia, and Egypt. Archaeologists have unearthed signs of as many as fifteen cities, one built on the forgotten ruins of another, centuries apart. Wars were almost continuous. Nations rose and fell and disappeared, and with them went much of their culture and knowledge. This is found in the history of Rome as well, which six times was overcome by "barbarians." Libraries and public buildings, with their records, were razed to the ground in this destruction. This was the fate of the great city of Alexandria, with its treasured library; and of Constantinople, founded by Constantine the Great, the center of culture for a thousand years.

The Rosetta Stone

The early history of Egypt and its discoveries and knowledge were recorded in hieroglyphics, a method of writing with some six hundred picture characters, used by the priesthood and by learned Egyptians. These were engraved on stone monuments and tombs. By 3000 B.C., the Egyptians had also developed an alphabet of twenty-four characters called hieratic, which could be written with a reed pen on papyrus, the Egyptian paper, and which was also used by the priesthood. By 2 B.C., demotic, a simplified form of hieratic, was developed for use of the common people. Until the end of the eighteenth century, the meaning of these writings was unknown to European scholars, and much of what we know about ancient Egypt dates back only to about 1850. The key that unlocked the puzzle was the famed Rosetta stone, which now reposes in the British Museum in London.

On May 19, 1798, General Napoleon Bonaparte set sail from Toulon for Egypt, with not only soldiers and guns, but a university's complement of 175 learned men—astronomers, geometricians, antiquarians, Orientalists, poets, and painters. The campaign progressed well until August 1, when the French fleet was found in Abukir Bay by an English fleet under Admiral Nelson, and all but two ships of the line and two frigates were either captured or destroyed. When the invasion bogged down, Napoleon's technicians swarmed here and there, studying everything. The buried temples of Upper Egypt were uncovered, the Wells of Moses were discovered. The results of their scientific investigations were later recorded in thirty-six printed volumes. The campaign was a military failure, but a scientific triumph.

Most important of the discoveries was a slab of black basalt, a volcanic stone, which was found by Boussard, a French engineer-officer, about four miles from the village of Rosetta. The stone contains three blocks of engraved texts in three totally different styles of characters: hieroglyphic, used by the priesthood; demotic, the form of writing employed by the common people; and Greek, to communicate the message to foreigners. The Rosetta stone was sent to Paris, where the French scholar Jean François Champollion began to study it. He had previously discovered that demotic was written with an alphabet. By intercomparing the three inscriptions, he found that they were an identical decree of the priests, stating that for his good works, statues of Ptolemy V. Epiphanes, ruler of Egypt, were to be set up, to which divine honors were to be paid, and warning of the perils of desecration. In this way, the hidden meaning of the hieroglyphics was found, and the history of Egypt engraved on its tombs and monuments could once again be read. In much the same way, other monuments with inscriptions in other ancient lost languages have been deciphered in modern times.

Hence, the story of time is not a record of continuous progress. Inventions and discoveries were made, then lost, and in some later period, perhaps after the passage of centuries, were rediscovered. There were few means of communication. The knowledge of one community was unknown a few hundred miles away.

For countless centuries, time and timekeeping were the special domain of priests and royal people. Observation of the stars served the needs of the priest-astrologer. A general knowledge of timekeeping among ordinary people hardly goes back two hundred years. Such knowledge was unnecessary until the social organization of the world began to approach the tightly integrated society of today.

Primitive Divisions of Time

The first of the five Books of Moses of the Old Testament sheds light on early timekeeping methods. This great man of the Jewish people is believed to have lived in the thirteenth or fourteenth century B.C. He is believed to have received an education comparable to that of the priests of Egypt. In Genesis, we find:

> 1:5. And God called the light Day, and the darkness he called Night. And the evening and the morning were the first day. . . .
> 14. And God said, Let there be lights in the firmament of the heaven to divide the day from the night; and let them be for signs, and for seasons, and for days, and years. . . .
> 16. And God made two great lights; the greater light to rule the day, and the lesser light to rule the night: he made the stars also.
> 17. And God set them in the firmament of the heaven to give light upon the earth,
> 18. And to rule over the day and over the night, and to divide the light from the darkness: and God saw that it was good.

The sun, the moon, and the seasons—these were timepieces which all could read. The words in Genesis: "And the evening and the morning were the first day" reveal the custom of counting the passage of "days" by nights. Nights were the time to hide from fearsome beasts and vile men. How welcome must have seemed the first flush of dawn after a night without light, or perhaps only

that from the feeble glow of the embers of a fire. Even when the daylight, from
sunrise to sunset, began to be divided into hours at the beginning of the Christian Era, the nights were divided into "watches," as for centuries before. Biblical reference is found in Matthew 14:25: "in the fourth watch of the night."
A watch was three or four hours long, depending on the time of year. "In the
watches of the night" is a phrase still frequently met in poetic works.

Primitive agricultural people had little use for timepieces or calendars. "I
will meet you when the sun is *there*" set the time with sufficient accuracy for
all purposes. Those who live in the country see the modern farmer, just as the
ancient one might have done, stop his work close to the hour of noon, actually
within minutes of solar noon, without benefit of a watch. Living close to nature, pastoral people read the signs of the changing seasons all about them.
The observation that swallows come and leave within a matter of days, year
after year, is found in the most ancient literature. The southern flight of birds,
first of one variety and then another, gives repeated warning of the coming of
fall and winter, just as their return is a happy prelude to spring. As this season
advances, the growth and blossoming of wild flowers and grasses records the
passage of time with amazing exactness. Farmers in our northern states today
solemnly advise not to plant corn "until the leaves of the oak are the size of a
squirrel's ear," and probably similar admonitions have guided the planting of
crops since earliest times.

The Roman Day

Among the Romans of 500 B.C., as noted by Pliny in his *Natural History,* only
the sunrise and sunset were marked. Then the public crier announced these
events from the senate house. At a later date, noon was announced "when the
Consul's apparitor saw the sun between the Beaks and the Greek lodging."
He announced the last hour "when the sun sloped from the Maenian Column
to the prison." Not until 159 B.C. were the hours of daylight marked for the
Roman public.

The custom of dividing the day into twenty-four hours was little known by
the average man until around A.D. 1600. Our Saxon ancestors divided the day
into "tides," from which the words "morningtide," "noontide," and "eventide" remain as poetic souvenirs. Noontide was roughly the interval between
10:30 A.M. and 1:30 P.M.; eventide was from 1:30 P.M. to 4:30 P.M. A sundial
believed to have been made in the year A.D. 1064, and marked in tides, is
preserved in the Kirkdale Church in Yorkshire, England.

At the beginning of the Christian Era, the Romans divided the day into five
periods, or "hours." In A.D. 605, Pope Sabinianus added two more hours to
the Roman arrangement and decreed that the bells of the churches were to be
rung at these times. These are the seven canonical hours, and they dominated
the life of Europe for centuries. The seven canonical hours were the only form

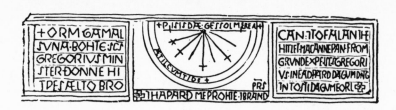

Saxon sundial of A.D. 1064 in the churchyard of the Kirkdale Church in Yorkshire, England, indicating the "tides" into which the Saxon day was divided.

of "time" observed on the ships of Columbus. To keep them in order, a half-hour sandglass was turned as it emptied. The seven canonical hours still constitute, with some modification, the hours of service for the Roman and Anglican churches. They were: matins (morning) and lauds (praise), prime (first), tierce (third), sext (sixth), nones (ninth), vespers (evening), and complin (complete). Matins and lauds are today usually combined in the first service of the morning with recitations of psalms in praise of God. Prime, the first division of the Roman day, approximately 6:00 A.M., became the second canonical hour. Tierce, the second hour of the Roman day, about 9:00 A.M., marks the third service. Sext, the third hour of the Roman day, about noon, is the fourth service. Nones, the fourth hour, about 3:00 P.M., is the fifth service. Vespers is usually held late afternoon or evening, with complin the final Roman and canonical hour.

Among the earliest people, the inability to count would have precluded any conception of weeks, months, or years. Anthropologists deduce that a custom followed by primitive tribes to this day probably represents the earliest method of counting in ancient times. Three ages of man are their recognized birthdays. The first age is boys and girls too young to work; the second age is men and women able to do the work ordered for them in the tribe; the third age, made up of those too old to work, are simply known as "once-men" and "once-women." Among certain people, the once-men and once-women are either killed, or as with the Eskimo, left alone with a small store of food in an igloo by their "last campfire."

The idea of weeks, months, and years had to wait for the beginning of astronomy and the growth of religion. The whole prelude to the system of organized timekeeping was to be created by these forces. For the common man, timekeeping remained a simple and logical matter of observation of the world in which he lived, until the coming of the Industrial Revolution. Then it advanced rapidly, as one technological discovery followed another, and means of communication became more swift, until we find ourselves caught and governed by the rigid timekeeping system which man has evolved over the years, and which in today's society is so essential.

CHAPTER II

Magic and Religion

The Celestial Deities

THROUGHOUT all his past, man has been plagued with afflictions—accidents, floods, earthquakes, bolts of lightning, wars, and so on. And as today, asked, "Why does this happen to me?" Almost all looked into the vastness of the firmament for answers. The names of the days of the week, the month names of our calendar, and the calendar itself reflect their origin in ancient superstitions, in celestial deities, in gods and goddesses, and in magic and religion.

Primitive divisions of time were associated with the celestial deities. The obelisk of the Egyptians was the symbol of the sun god Ra. Hundreds of these were erected throughout Egypt, particularly around the once great city of Heliopolis in lower Egypt near the present city of Cairo, and in Thebes. In Heliopolis, so it is said, Moses studied law. The earliest known obelisks date back to around 3100 B.C. The so-called Cleopatra's Needle in Central Park in New York City, and that in Trafalgar Square in London, originally flanked the entrance to the Temple of the Sun at Heliopolis, where they were erected by the Pharaoh Thutmose III, around 1500 B.C. You who may admire the New York obelisk may like to know how it got there.

It was removed from Heliopolis by the Roman emperor Augustus in 12 B.C., and erected with its twin at the entrance to the Caesarium, the Temple of the Caesars, in Alexandria. It was probably at this date that it acquired the sobriquet Cleopatra's Needle, the queen at this time being enamoured with Mark Anthony, with whom Augustus was fueding for the control of Rome. In 1880, on the occasion of the opening of the Suez Canal, the khedive of Egypt offered the two obelisks to the cities of New York and London. The cost of moving the New York obelisk and re-erecting it amounted to $102,576, which was donated by William H. Vanderbilt. The hieroglyphics on the New York obelisk pay tribute to the celestial origin of Thutmose III, ruler of Upper and Lower Egypt. Some three centuries later, Ramses II also proclaimed his kinship with Ra by columns of hieroglyphics carved on the same monument. When first erected at Heliopolis, the pyramidion was covered with gold metal.

From a study of the shadows of the obelisk, the Egyptians found the length of the year. They discovered the summer and winter solstices. The summer solstice occurs about June 21, when the altitude of the sun at noon reaches its highest point, and the shadow of the obelisk is shortest. This is the longest day of the year. At the winter solstice, the shadow of the obelisk is longest. This occurs about December 21, when the altitude of the sun is at its lowest point, and marks the shortest day of the year. Between these two points, at about March 21 and September 21, which we call the vernal (spring) and autumn equinoxes, they found day and night were of equal length.

Many people of the ancient world marked these dates by fetes or religious observances. The celebrations of Easter and Christmas, which occur about the times of the vernal equinox and winter solstice, had counterparts in Egypt, Persia, India, pagan Rome, and also among the Aztecs of South America. When the Spanish conquistadors witnessed Aztec ceremonies dedicated to their sun god, they branded them as heathen counterfeits of Christian sacraments.

Easter and the Paschal Moon

The celebration of Easter parallels the spring festivals observed since earliest days. Such celebrations were dated to occur at the first full moon of spring. In ancient days this was a logical choice of time. Before the coming of the general illumination to which we are accustomed today, the light of the moon had a value second only to that of the sun. The full moon which shines from dusk to dawn provided light by which pilgrims could travel through the night if necessary to get to their places of worship.

The Jewish calendar originally began the year at the vernal equinox, about March 21, and it was ordained in Exodus that the Passover should be held on the fourteenth day of the first month of the ecclesiastical year. Because of the relationship of the Last Supper to the Jewish Passover, the early Christian Church made Easter concur with it, but it was arranged that they were not to occur on the same day.

The rule fixing the date of Easter was established in A.D. 325, during the reign of Emperor Constantine, when the Council of Nicaea (Nice) ordered that Easter be celebrated on the first Sunday after the first "full moon," the Paschal moon, following the vernal equinox. The date of the Paschal full moon may not correspond to that of the actual full moon by a day or so. It is determined by the use of what is called the Metonic cycle, a period of about 19 years, in which the *new* moon returns to the same day of the month. It was named after its discoverer, the Greek astronomer Meton. The Metonic cycle of 19 years,

The obelisk, symbol of the Egyptian sun god Ra.
The Greeks called it a gnomon (one who knows).

which consists of 235 lunations, is longer than 19 years by about 2 hours and 6 minutes, which is eliminated by the starting of a new Metonic cycle. When the scheme was instituted, the first Metonic cycle was assumed to have begun on the year preceding the first year of the Christian Era.

The Golden Number

To January 1 of each year is assigned the number on which it occurred during a Metonic cycle, and this is called its Golden Number. Most almanacs, even to-day, give the Golden Number for the year. For centuries (and perhaps now), the Golden Number had special significance, and many superstitions were evolved around it. However, it is from the Golden Number that the first full moon on or next following the vernal equinox is found, by means of a table. The vernal equinox is specified as falling on March 21.

To aid in the calculations, each year is given a Dominical Letter. The days of the week are named from the first seven letters of the alphabet, starting the first "week" on January 1. The Dominical Letter for the year is the letter which marks the first Sunday after January 1. By this means, the Dominical Letter for any year can be found, and from this can be determined what day of the week it was or will be for any date. These provisions and tables for the calculation of dates, introduced with the adoption of the Gregorian calendar, made it possible for the Church Fathers without knowledge of astronomy to fix Easter Sunday and, by so doing, establish other movable holy days of the year, since they are all tied to Easter.

The day of the new moon does not occur on the same day and at the same time in all parts of the world; nor does the vernal equinox always fall on March 21. However, these are matters which are of primary concern only to astronomers.

The Bible says nothing about the date of the birth of Christ, and early Christians did not celebrate it. The first celebration of the Nativity was instituted by Christian residents in Egypt, who observed January 6 as Christmas. The present custom of celebrating Christmas on December 25 was instituted in A.D. 375.

The Gods of the Sky

The worship of the sun and moon among early people was almost universal. To the Persians, the sun god was Mithras, ruler also of the moon and stars. The Babylonians worshipped a trio of deities: Sin, Shamash, and Adad, ruling respectively the moon, sun, and atmosphere. The sun god of the Phoenicians was Baal, and the moon goddess, Astarte, queen of the heavens. Among the three thousand-odd deities of the Hindus were Surya, the sun god, and Indra, his moon goddess.

From the Homeric poems we learned that to the Greeks the sun god was the dazzling Apollo. Each morning as Aurora, goddess of the dawn, held open the purple gates, Apollo mounted his golden chariot and, drawn by horses of burnished gold, rode his appointed arched course through the sky. The world was then believed to be flat. In the Old Testament, in Ecclesiastes 1:5, we find: "The sun also ariseth, and the sun goeth down, and hasteth to his place where he arose." The moon goddess of the Greeks was the virgin Diana, whose chariot was of silver drawn by maidens in flowing white robes. Volumes of prose and some of the most beautiful poetry have been inspired by the celestial creations of mystified ancient minds.

English thought has been influenced by Norse mythology in which the chief god was Odin (Mercury), also spelled Woden, from which is derived the name Wednesday. The eldest son of Woden was Thor (Jupiter), strongest of the Norse gods and ruler of the day which we call Thursday. The wife of Woden was Frigg or Freya (Venus), friend of lovers, who presided over the rain and sunshine and the fruiting of the earth. From Frigg comes the word Friday. The division of the months into weeks was not, however, an early development in timekeeping.

The counting of the days, the moon's phases, and the seasons were the first divisions of time. The origin of the word month, from moon, is obvious. The ancient keepers of time were the priests and astrologers. It was their responsibility to know the portents of the stars. The kings and nobles in whose services they toiled, also looked to the priests and astrologers for means of calculating the time to collect taxes and interest. The astrologers laid the foundation for modern astronomy and the science of timekeeping. Those millions of us living in the city, with the murk and dust of industry and the glare of countless neon signs and electric lights which put a film over our vision, have no notion of the majestic spectacle of the heavens which must have been regarded with awe by primitive people. On a high mountain on a clear winter night one sees the millions of stars gleaming in the transparent blue vault of the sky, as the ancients did. It is a vision of indescribable splendor. From a darkened ship at sea, or from the cockpit of a high aircraft, the starry heaven is also seen in all its glory. Those with almost no knowledge of astronomy recognize the Big Dipper, and any Boy or Girl Scout, by consulting the Big Dipper, can locate the polestar for you. The Big Dipper appears to make a complete circle around the polestar in twenty-four hours.

The Zodiac and Astrology

Before the days of watches, the motion of the circumpolar stars was common knowledge, even among ordinary people. It was their clock in the sky. The whole of the heavens appears to rotate slowly in a westerly direction. Lower down toward the horizon, the apparent motion of the stars becomes very slow.

The Clock in the Sky. Familiar to every school child is the constellation Ursa Major (Great Bear) which is more commonly called the Big Dipper in the United States, the Plough in England, and the Big Wagon in Germany. The Big Dipper makes almost, but not quite, a complete turn around the Polestar every twenty-four hours, the change every six hours is almost 45°. In ancient days observant country folk could tell time by the Big Dipper, which in Shakespeare's time was known as Charles's Wain (wagon). The Nocturnal (see Chapter VI) was an instrument designed to tell time from "The Clock in the Sky."

Some stars are found in groups or constellations. These lay in a belt closely following the apparent path of the sun. The ancients saw in these star groups the forms of living things. The belt is called the zodiac, from the Greek *zodiakos,* meaning animal: zodiac, the belt of the animals. They observed that in the course of a year, the twelve constellations appeared one by one in almost equal intervals: first Aries, the Ram, in December; then Taurus, the Bull; followed by Gemini, the Twins; Cancer, the Crab; Leo, the Lion, in late March and early April; Virgo, the Virgin; Libra, the Balance or Scales; Scorpio, the Scorpion; Sagittarius, the Archer. Scorpio and Sagittarius only come into view low on the horizon in northern temperate latitudes during the summer, and they were the signs during July and August. Next in line is Capricorn, the Sea Goat; followed by Aquarius, the Water Carrier; and finally, Pisces, the Fishes. These signs of the zodiac were used by the Hindus to name the months.

The constellations in the zodiac moved with the heavenly dome as though fastened to it, as in truth the ancients believed. But certain lights or stars took their own path; sometimes moving with the rest of the stars, sometimes moving ahead of them, sometimes appearing to move backward. In general, they moved eastward amid the constellations of the zodiac, overtaking them until they returned to their starting point. They named these stars wanderers, or *planets*. Among them they included the sun and the moon which, though not planets, move in the path of the zodiac. The others were Mercury, Mars, Venus, Jupiter, and Saturn. One sign of the zodiac was dominant at each period of the year, and the appearance or proximity of one of the planets to the sign was an "omen." The interpretation of the stars occupied the minds of astronomers to the time of Kepler (1571-1630), and judging by the preoccupation of many people with astrology, still casts a spell. The picture, in old almanacs, of a nude man with lines running from the signs of the zodiac to various parts of his anatomy, indicated the points where a patient should be bled according to the time of the year. These bleeding points were observed by physicians until our Civil War time.

How the Days of the Week Were Named

We recognize in the names of the planets, the names of three days of the week —Sunday, the day of the sun; Monday, the day of the moon; and Saturday, the day of Saturn. Though these names were adopted in comparatively recent times, their origin is most ancient. The Quakers, who would have no part of this heathen practice, gave numbers to the days of the week. Sunday is first day.

The names of the seven days of the week were once related to the seven ages of man, as they still are in India: the Sun, giver of life, was the symbol of birth; the Moon, goddess of fertility, governed infancy; adolescence was dominated by Venus, goddess of love; Mercury, god of learning, governed young manhood; Mars, the god of war, governed adult manhood; middle age was ruled by Jupiter, symbolizing wisdom and knowledge; old age was ruled by Saturn, the malignant luminary that foretold death. Among the Greeks, one of these planet gods was assigned to govern each day.

Though the Babylonians had a seven-day week, as discovered recently by archaeologists, and as the Jews have had from their earliest days, as prescribed by the Scriptures, the seven-day week was first introduced into Europe as a division of time by Constantine the Great in A.D. 321, at which time Sunday was named Sabbath by the Christian Church. Weeks were unknown before that date, and among ordinary people, were not observed until much later. The earliest division of time appears to have occurred through market days. In various communities, every fourth or fifth day, or some other period, would be Market Day, when people came from the country to trade goods with those in the cities. There have been "weeks" of four days, five days, eight days, and ten days observed in various parts of the world. The Greeks at one time had a ten-day week called a Decade, a name we now give to a period of ten years.

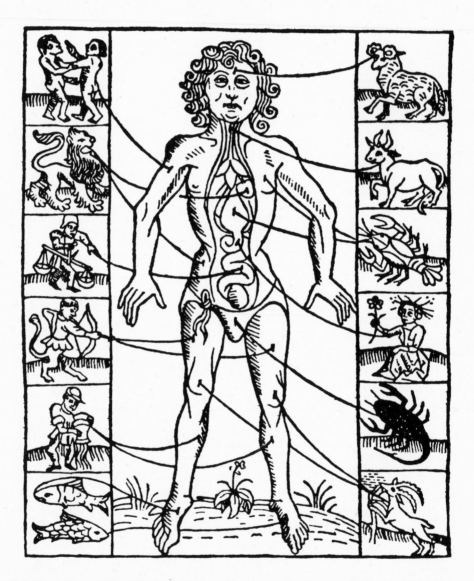

Bleeding Points. This illustration, found in many old almanacs, told the doctor where his patient should be bled according to the prevailing sign of the zodiac, a custom followed up to our Civil War days.

Beware the Ides of March

Shakespeare displayed an unusual knowledge of the chronology of ancient Rome when, in *Julius Caesar,* he made dramatic use of the line of the Soothsayer: "Beware the ides of March"; and later in the play, when Caesar said to him, "The ides of March are come," to which the Soothsayer replied, "Ay, Caesar; but not gone." The Romans at this period divided months in a most peculiar fashion. The first day of each month was called its *Kalendae,* from which the word calendar derives. The day before the end of the month was known as *Pridie Kalendae.* Thus, the day before the first of February was *Pridie Kalendae Februariae.* The midmonth day was the *Ides,* which varied from the thirteenth day to the fifteenth day, depending on the number of days in the month. The *Ides* of March was March 15. Similarly, the fifth or seventh day was the *Nones.* So, counting *Kalendae* as the first of March, for example, the second to sixth days were called the second to sixth day *before the Nones;* the following days, so many *before the Ides;* and then again, so many days before the *Pridie Kalendae* of the following month. It was a simple arrangement that must have produced enormous complications.

The origins of the names of the days of the week have already been mentioned. It is one of the unexplained mysteries of time that in most of the basic languages, the same gods served to name the same days of the week in the same order, as seen in the following tabulation:

DAYS OF WEEK IN DIFFERENT LANGUAGES

ORIGIN	SAXON	SPANISH	LATIN	SANSKRIT	BABYLONIAN
Sun	Sun's Day	Domingo	Dies Solis	Ravi vara	Shamash
Moon	Moon's Day	Lunes	Dies Lunae	Soma vara	Sin
Mars	Tiw's Day	Martes	Dies Martis	Mangala vara	Nergal
Mercury	Woden's Day	Miércoles	Dies Mercurii	Budha vara	Nabu
Jupiter	Thor's Day	Jueves	Dies Jovis	Brihaspati vara	Marduk
Venus	Frigg's Day	Viernes	Dies Veneris	Shukra vara	Ishtar
Saturn	Saterne's Day	Sábado	Dies Saturni	Sanischara vara	Ninib

CHAPTER III

The Evolution of the Calendar

The Calendar of Romulus

OUR PRESENT CALENDAR represents an evolution from a series of Roman calendars, the first of which was instituted about 738 B.C. by King Romulus, founder of Rome. The complete calendar of Romulus consisted of 10 months. It began on the date the vernal equinox was then celebrated, March 25 according to the present calendar, and ended about our January 24, making a year of 304 days. The balance of the 61 days to make up a year as we know it, was not counted. This calendar is believed to have been patterned after that followed in primitive areas in the north, where the deepest months of winter, being useless, were simply ignored. Most of the names of the months of the Romulus calendar have been perpetuated in the calendar of today. The first month of the Romulus calendar was named *Martius* after Mars, the god of war. The second month, *Aprilis,* was derived from the Latin *aperire,* meaning "to open," suggesting the period of budding leaves and opening flowers. The third month was *Maius,* after Maia, the goddess of growth. The fourth month was *Junius,* from *juvenis,* youth. The remaining 6 months were given numerical names: *Quintilis* (fifth), *Sextilis* (sixth), *Septembris* (seventh), *Octobris* (eighth), *Novembris* (ninth), and *Decembris* (tenth).

The Numa Calendar

Romulus was succeeded, around 713 B.C., by King Numa Pompilius who introduced a calendar based on lunar cycles, and added 2 new months to make a year of 12 months. The first of the 2 new months was named *Januarius,* after Janus, guardian of the heavens and protector of gateways, symbolizing the beginning, and was placed ahead of Martius. The second new month was called *Februarius,* named for Februalia, meaning repentance, a period when sacrifices were to be made to the gods for offenses committed during the year. It was made the last month of the year, and followed Decembris.

The calendar of King Numa continued the beginning of the new year at the vernal equinox. Even numbers were considered unlucky, so they arranged 7 months of 29 days, 4 months of 31 days, and the leftover 28 days were given to Februarius, which signaled the death of the year, and not too lucky anyway. The year had 355 days. It was soon found that this 10-day shortage was making the vernal equinox 10 days earlier year after year. To correct this, an extra month of 22 or 23 days, which was called *Mercedonius,* was introduced into the calendar every other year. This system did not coincide with the true length of the solar year, as was later determined.

The Numa calendar had a life of something less than three hundred years. In 450 B.C., the Council of Decemvirs, under Appius Claudius, reshuffled the months and placed the keeping of the calendar under the Pontifical College. It was at this time that Februarius was taken from the end of the calendar and placed between Januarius and Martius, making the year end with the month Decembris.

The Julian Calendar Adopted from the Egyptians

It must be remembered that there was no publication of this calendar. It was kept by the priests, who announced the time for celebrations and the time for the collection of taxes, interest, and rentals, from which profits could be made by tinkering with it. The number of days in the various months was changed at will. The calendar became so mutilated that it no longer kept time with the seasons. The strong hand necessary to effect a drastic reform in the calendar appeared when Julius Caesar seized power in Rome and assumed the office of Pontifex Maximus. He thus became the leader of the state religion, in whose domain the calendar fell. The reform of the Roman calendar, ordered by Julius Caesar, was placed in the hands of the Alexandrian astronomer Sosigenes. In order to put the new calendar into effect, Caesar ordered a preliminary year of 445 days for the purpose of adjusting the calendar to the seasons. This has since become known as the "year of confusion." The calendar, as finally adopted, was essentially that of the Egyptian calendar then prevailing.

The Egyptians had observed a similar lunar calendar for close to four thousand years, with several differences. They began their year at about our July 19, a date which signaled two important events—the rising of the Dog Star Sirius (the Egyptian god Sothis), which appeared in the east just before dawn; and the annual flooding of the Nile, which covered the sand with rich silt and made possible the planting of grain, from which the wealth of the country came. At this period, their months were 30 days long; their year covered 360 days. Over the years, the Egyptians found that a calendar based on lunar cycles caused the beginning of their new year and the flooding of the Nile to get out of date. The average length of the lunar cycle is 29.53059 days. A lunar year of 12 lunations is 354 days, roughly, or exactly *plus* 8 hours, 48 minutes, and 34 seconds. From their study of the shadows of the obelisk, they established the length of the solar year as 365¼ days. Around 238 B.C., 5 extra days were added to the end of the year, each a holiday; and the practice of inserting extra days in leap years was also introduced. The story of how the Egyptians corrected their calendar is told by Plutarch, the historian, somewhat in these words:

> When the sun-god Ra perceived that his wife Nut had been unfaithful to him, he declared with a curse that she should be delivered of the child in no month and no year! But the goddess had another lover, the god, Thoth . . . and he playing at draughts with the moon won from her a seventy-second part of every day, and having compounded five whole days out of these parts he added them to the Egyptian year of three hundred and sixty days. (From *Adonis, Attis, Osiris,* II, p. 6, in *The Golden Bough,* Sir James George Frazer.)

This mythical story serves to explain the underlying part of magic and religion in the early development of time measurements.

The Julian calendar was based on the estimate of the year's length as 365¼ days. Caesar changed Quintilis, the seventh month, to *Julius,* in his own honor. The months became: Januarius, Martius, Maius, Julius, Septembris, and Novembris with 31 days each; Aprilis, Junius, Sextilis, Octobris, and Decembris were months of 30 days. Februarius was to have 29 days in common years, and 30 days in leap years, or every fourth year. The new year started on January 1 instead of March 25. The new Julian calendar went into effect in 47 B.C., according to our present method of calculating.

With the death of Caesar, the Pontifical College, once more without effective leadership, again started tinkering with the calendar. For a period of 36 years, they made leap year every third year instead of every fourth, as the calendar had been planned.

The calendar was again reformed by Augustus Caesar in 8 B.C. It was brought into line by eliminating the leap years between 8 B.C. and A.D. 8. Then, following the precedent of Julius Caesar, Augustus also renamed a month in his honor. The old month Sextilis became *Augustus.* To avoid having ill luck associated with the even number of days assigned to this month, he added an extra day, taking it away from Februarius. Although radically changed by Augustus, the name Julian is customarily given to the calendar.

Origin of the Counting of the Christian Era

The next change took place in A.D. 532, when the Abbott of Rome, Dionysius Exiguus, acknowledging the then current tradition of recognizing March as the month of Annunciation, named March 25 as the date of the conception of Christ, and further ordered that henceforth the year was to begin on that date, which also determined the birth date of Christ as December 25. This was a radical innovation which was followed for over a thousand years. Dionysius is also credited with having established the Christian Era from the presumed date of the birth of Christ, and thus began the custom of counting historical periods B.C., before Christ, and A.D., *anno Domini,* the year of our Lord.

The Gregorian Calendar

In A.D. 532, when the Christian holidays were set, the calendar seemed to have everything well in hand. There was, however, a trivial error in the calculation of the actual length of the year. The calendar was based on the assumption that the year is 365.25 days long. Actually, the solar year is 365.2422 days, a difference of 0.0078 day in a whole year; a day in 128 years. While the vernal equinox occurred on March 21 in A.D. 325, this celestial phenomenon, knowing nothing of man-made calendars, retreated to March 15 in the year A.D. 1093, and in due time, if nothing had been done about it, would have taken place at Christmas. The Council of Trent of 1582 authorized the Pope to rectify this unfortunate state of affairs, and after consultation with many astronomers, Gregory XIII ordered that the day following Thursday, October 4, 1582, would be Friday, October 15, 1582. He changed the beginning of the year from March 25 to January 1, as Numa had instituted 2,295 years previously. The change was not followed by England and the Colonies until 1752, by which time the old Augustan calendar had accumulated another day's error. So our country has no history between Wednesday, September 2, 1752, and Thursday, September 14, 1752. Eleven days—gone with the wind! That is why the birthday of Washington, born February 11 on the old style calendar is today celebrated on the 22nd. Of the loss of days necessary to put the new calendar in use, Benjamin Franklin wrote in his *Almanack:*

> Be not astonished, nor look with scorn, dear reader, at such a deduction of days, nor regret as for the loss of so much time, but take this for your consolation, that your expenses will appear lighter and your mind be more at ease. And what an indulgence is here, for those who love their pillow to lie down in Peace on the second of this month and not perhaps awake till the morning of the fourteenth.

With the adoption of the new calendar, England and the Colonies, which had observed March 25 as New Year's Day, switched to our present January 1.

The Gregorian calendar, which we now follow, outwardly differs from the Augustan only in the dropping of 3 leap-year days every 4 centuries. Thus, 1700, 1800, and 1900 were not leap years. The year 2000 will be. The general rule is that 3 century years in every 400 years that are not divisible by 400 will be common years. The prime purpose of the Gregorian calendar was to control the date of Easter Sunday. This is so detailed that an explanation of the calendar written by Clavius who, with the astronomer Luigi Lilio Ghiraldi developed it, covers a great folio treatise of six hundred pages, published in

1603. (The Gregorian calendar is not perfect, but is still an amazingly accurate timekeeper. Its error is calculated as 26 seconds per year, which would add up to a whole day in 3,323 years.)

DEVELOPMENT OF THE ROMAN CALENDAR

ROMULUS 738 B.C.	NUMA 713 B.C.	COUNCIL OF DECEMVIRS 451 B.C.	JULIUS 47 B.C.	AUGUSTUS 8 B.C.	GREGORY XIII EUROPE A.D. 1582 ENGLAND A.D. 1752
Martius 31	Januarius 29	Januarius 29	Januarius 31	Januarius 31	January 31
Aprilis 30	Martius 31	Februarius 28	Februarius 29–30	Februarius 28–29	February 28–29
Maius 31	Aprilis 29	Martius 31	Martius 31	Martius 31	March 31
Junius 30	Maius 31	Aprilis 29	Aprilis 30	Aprilis 30	April 30
Quintilis 31	Junius 29	Maius 31	Maius 31	Maius 31	May 31
Sextilis 30	Quintilis 31	Junius 29	Junius 30	Junius 30	June 30
Septembris 31	Sextilis 29	Quintilis 31	Julius 31	Julius 31	July 31
Octobris 30	Septembris 29	Sextilis 29	Sextilis 30	Augustus 31	August 31
Novembris 31	Octobris 31	Septembris 29	Septembris 31	Septembris 30	September 30
Decembris 29	Novembris 29	Octobris 31	Octobris 30	Octobris 31	October 31
	Decembris 29	Novembris 29	Novembris 31	Novembris 30	November 30
	Februarius 28	Decembris 29	Decembris 30	Decembris 31	December 31
304 days	355 days	355 days	365¼ days	365¼ days	365.2422 days

The First Almanacs

Publication of the calendar in Europe in the form of manuscript almanacs, cannot be traced back much before the thirteenth century, although they existed at a much earlier date in China, as we will see later. The first printed almanac of record is that of the astronomer Purbach, which was published in Vienna in 1457. General publication of calendars in the form of almanacs began in England around 1600, the most famous of which was *Poor Robin's Almanack*. All of these early almanacs, much like those of the present day, contained astrological information, home remedies for man and beast, weather prognostications, advice to one and sundry, and homilies for guidance of the reader in all matters of human life. In many early calendars, symbols were used for dates to make them readable to the illiterate. The first calendar published in the United States is believed to have been printed by William Bradford in Philadelphia in 1687. Benjamin Franklin began the publication of *Poor Richard's Almanack* in 1732, and it was continued for about twenty-five years.

Chinese Almanacs

Marco Polo wrote: "In the city of Cambaluc there are some 5000 astrologers and soothsayers, whom the Great Kaan provides with annual maintenance, and they are in the constant exercise of their art. They have a kind of Astrolabe on which are inscribed the planetary signs, the hours and critical points of the whole year, by which they investigate the course and character of the whole year according to the indications of each of its Moons, in order to discover by the natural course and disposition of the planets, and the other circumstances of the heavens, what shall be the nature of the weather, and what peculiarities shall be produced by each Moon of the year; as for example, under which Moon there shall be thunderstorms and tempests, under which there shall be disease, murrain, wars, disorders, and treasons, and so on according to the indications of each. And they write down the results of their examination in certain little pamphlets for the year, which are called *Tacuin*.

"And if anyone having some great matter in hand, or proposing to make a long journey for traffic or other business, desires to know what will be the upshot, he goes to one of the astrologers and says: 'Turn up your books and see what is the present aspect of the heavens.' " (From *The Book of Marco Polo.*)

These little pamphlets were almanacs, and it is said that the Mongol year to which Marco Polo refers was adopted from the Chinese system which was originated during the reign of Emperor Hwang-ti in 2637 B.C. The calendar was based on twelve "Earthly Branches," which served to name not only the months, but days and hours as well. They bore the names: Rat, Ox, Tiger, Hare, Dragon, Serpent, Horse, Sheep, Ape, Cock, Dog, and Swine. Since each represented a cycle of the moon, a number of supplementary days termed the

"Heavenly Stems" were added, so that a period of sixty years separated the appearance of the same month with the same qualifying "Heavenly Stem." The modifying words were taken from the names of the elements: Wood, Fire, Earth, Water, Iron; or from the names of colors: Blue, Red, Yellow, White, Black.

Almanacs were printed by the government, and it was a prison offense to issue one privately. As early as A.D. 1328, some three million copies were printed and distributed, according to an old writer. The publication of the almanac by the Chinese over the years might be considered as a form of "thought control," and part of the program of assuring civil obedience. The almanacs marked the lucky and unlucky days, the best days for getting married, for undertaking a journey, for making a dress, for buying or building, and other activities of daily life.

The author recalls a conversation with a man who went to China in the twenties to open an office. He was told that the position of the desks could not be determined without consulting a soothsayer, and that the office could not be opened except on the day which an astrologer would name. We cannot, however, credit the Chinese for this superstition. It is believed that their astronomy and astrological interpretations were originally learned from Europeans, Arabians, or Persians.

The Greek Olympiads

The Olympic games, which are held every 4 years, are a souvenir of the Greek method of chronology which was adopted around the third century B.C. The Olympiads, or 4-year periods, at that time were dated back to the restoration of the ancient games by Iphitus about 776 B.C. An Olympiad consisted of alternately 49 and 50 Greeks months. This was due to the fact that to adjust the calendar of 12 months, alternately of 29 and 30 days, it was necessary to introduce an extra month into every third year. Various adjustments had to be made in this scheme until the discovery of the Metonic cycle consisting of 235 lunations, or 19 years, mentioned also in connection with the dating of Easter. The Metonic cycle was used to make adjustments in the Greek system of chronology so long as the counting of Olympiads continued. When Dionysius Exiguus calculated the date of the birth of Christ, he placed it in the fourth year of the 194th Olympiad, or the 753rd from the founding of Rome. Astronomers of today seem to agree that he placed the date 4 years too late, but with the mixed-up chronology of the intervening 3 centuries and the absence of accurate written history, it can still be considered as a noteworthy achievement.

The Hebrew Calendar

The Hebrew calendar is now considered to have begun with the autumnal equinox, September 21, in the year 3761 B.C., the date of the creation of the world, according to the Book of Genesis of the Hebrew Scriptures. The letters A.M., *anno mundi*, the year of creation, identify the Hebraic dates. The calendar is based on the cycles of the moon, with 6 months of 29 days and 6 months of 30 days in the common year. Each day begins at sunset; each month begins at sunset on the day of the new moon—actually, the crescent moon. The important consideration is that solemn religious days must not fall on certain days prohibited by Mosaic and rabbinical laws. These are: New Year's Day (Rosh Hashana), Passover (Pesach), the Day of Atonement (Yom Kippur), Feast of Lots (Purim), and Pentecost (Shabuoth). To keep these religious festivals in order, an extra month of 29 days is added after Adar (called Veadar, or second Adar), 7 times in a cycle of 19 solar years. Veadar becomes the seventh month in the embolismic year, which has 13 months. The Jewish years, thus, have variously 353, 354, 355, 383, 384, and 385 days, following a complicated system of rules almost beyond the comprehension of lay people. As with all calendars which, in early days, were kept by priests for the use of priests in announcing the religious holidays, these complications are of little importance.

The Jewish world still orders its religious life according to this calendar, which will call the year 1960, A.M. 5721.

Calendar Improvement

The Gregorian calendar is a patchwork product involved with the whimsies of kings and dictators, which has grown out of the magic and religions of past ages, and a developing astronomical knowledge. Our present calendar, though reformed last within four hundred years, is not keeping step with either our knowledge or social needs. The improvement of the calendar is a matter of international concern. The basic weakness is the lack of rational division of its components—the year, the half year, the quarter, the month, and the week.

The solar year does not contain an integral number of days, consequently the calendar never agrees with the solar year from year to year. Consisting of 365 or 366 days, it is not possible to divide the year into equal halves, quarters, and twelfths.

The 12 divisions of the year are unequal. Months consist of 28, 29, 30, and 31 days, and any month can begin on any one of the 7 days of the week. The calendar does not provide for an integral number of weeks: in common years, there are 52 1/7 weeks; in leap years, 52 2/7 weeks.

In order to achieve desired time standardization to eliminate wasteful recording and cumbersome calculations caused by the Gregorian calendar, and to obtain comparative data relating to purchases, production, sales, costs, budgeting, labor turnover, overhead, and so forth, some twenty thousand firms in the United States alone have adopted a 13-month fiscal calendar. In the 13-month calendar, the months have 28 days, each month has 4 weeks, and each week is exactly like every other week, as shown by the following:

MONDAY	TUESDAY	WEDNESDAY	THURSDAY	FRIDAY	SATURDAY	SUNDAY
1	2	3	4	5	6	7
8	9	10	11	12	13	14
15	16	17	18	19	20	21
22	23	24	25	26	27	28

Another proposal, called the World calendar, provides uniformity of quarter-year periods. Both the 13-month fixed calendar, and the World calendar which has been brought before the United Nations, are superior to the Gregorian for practical modern use. Religious opposition is probably the greatest deterrent to calendar change.

The French Revolutionary Decimal Calendar

Typical of such resistance was that made to the Revolutionary calendar, which was brought about by the National Convention of Revolutionary France. The task of creating a new calendar was assigned to the president of the committee on public instruction Charles Gilbert Romme, the astronomer Pierre Simon Laplace, the mathematicians Gaspard Monge and Joseph Louis Lagrange, and the poet Fabre d'Eglantine. It was, in effect, a decimal calendar. The week of 7 days was replaced by a 10-day week, called a *décade*. Three *décades* comprised a month. The days of each *décade* were given Latin numerical names. Each day was divided into 10 hours, each hour into 100 minutes, each minute into 100 seconds. The 12 30-day months accounted for 360 days. The residual 5 or 6 added days were named in honor of the following, and celebrated on the dates indicated:

Les Vertus	(the virtues)	September 17
Le Génie	(the genius)	September 18
Le Travail	(the labor)	September 19
L'Opinion	(the opinion)	September 20
Les Récompenses	(the rewards)	September 21

The leap year days were called *Sans-culottides,* and were dedicated to sports. The first month of the calendar was to begin at midnight between September 21 and 22, near the autumnal equinox.

The Revolutionary Convention enacted the new calendar into law April 7, 1795, and it had a life of thirteen years. Unfortunately for its success, one of the announced purposes of this calendar was to eliminate the grip and influence of the Catholic Church, and it met with continuous resistance from Rome. Finally, with the ascension of Napoleon to the head of the government, he obtained the Pope's formal recognition of his personal authority over France and parts of conquered Europe, for which blessing he agreed to the death of the Revolutionary calendar and the rebirth of the Gregorian calendar, with its Saint's days and church holidays.

The Soviet Russia Experiments

Another example is found in Soviet Russia where, in 1929, the Union of Soviet Socialist Republics replaced the Gregorian calendar with one of their own. The announced purpose, again, was to destroy the influence of the church. Each month was to consist of 6 weeks of 5 days each. Each 5-day week was to have 4 working days, the fifth to be a free day. As in the case of the calendar of Revolutionary France, the extra 5 days of the normal year, and the 6 days of the leap year, were declared holidays.

In 1932, the Soviet calendar was changed to 12 months, each month consisting of 5 weeks of 6 days' duration. The months were named according to the Gregorian calendar, but the days of the week were identified merely by numbers. On June 27, 1940, the Soviet Union, as a result of many protests, abandoned its effort to have its own calendar, and adopted the Gregorian calendar.

In similar fashion, the Arab nations, which had followed the Mohammedan calendar, adopted the Gregorian calendar as their civil calendar, though reserving the Mohammedan calendar for religious use, as do the Jewish people.

The fact that many thousands of firms throughout the world are using the 13-month calendar for business purposes, while not interfering with the religious and other celebrations as dictated by the Gregorian calendar, suggests two calendars, one for religious and the other for civil use, as a means of effecting the change without incurring world-wide opposition.

The Julian Day of the Astronomers

The determination of the dates of past events is difficult, due to the chaotic chronology through the many calendars which have been used. For astronomical calculations, there is employed what is known as the Julian period, each period covering 7,980 years. The current Julian period began January 1 in the year 4713 B.C. The name of the period has nothing to do with Julius Caesar, but was applied in 1582 by its inventor, Joseph Scaliger, in honor of his father. In using the Julian period, it is customary to indicate dates by the total number of days that have elapsed since the beginning of the period, no reference being made to the years at all. The Julian day, identified with the initials *J.D.* is understood by all astronomers throughout the world, and the system is especially useful for obtaining the interval in days between two observations. Since the date of visibility of solar eclipses in various parts of the world can be readily estimated, historic dates can also be determined with great accuracy if there is a recorded eclipse in the same era.

For the calculation of dates according to Julian days, astronomers have reference to a table which assigns a number to each year. To this is added a month number representing the accumulation of days to the end of the prior month, and finally, the date of the month. For example, the year number for 1965 is 2,438,761, representing the number of days since the beginning of the present Julian period (4713 B.C.). If the date were March 25, we would add 59, representing the number of days in the year to the end of February; then 25, the number of days which have accumulated in March. According to Julian days, March 25, 1965 is 2,438,845.

CHAPTER IV

The Nature of Time

Our Natural Timepiece

OUR natural timepiece is the earth on which we live, its travels and turnings, and the apparent movement of the sun, moon, and heavenly bodies from the place where they are observed. The earth revolves on its own axis, making one revolution per day in a counterclockwise direction. The moon, a satellite of the earth, also rotates on its own axis and revolves around the earth, the time of rotation and revolution being substantially equal. It is for this reason that only one "face" of the moon is seen from the earth. A day and night on the moon is completed in about 27.32 of our days. As the earth revolves on its axis, it rotates around the sun in the same counterclockwise direction. The time required for the earth to make its course around the sun is what we call a year.

The axis of the earth is not perpendicular to the orbit of its rotation. If it were perpendicular, there would be relatively little difference in the temperature at the poles and at the equator, and there would be no seasons. The angle formed by the axis of the earth to its orbit of rotation is about 66.5°, or as sometimes given, the angle of the earth's equator to its orbit is 23.5°. The angle of the axis of the earth remains relatively constant during the rotation of the earth around the sun. Alternately, therefore, the north polar axis of the earth points toward the sun, and then away from it. When the axis points toward the sun, the northern parts of the earth have spring and summer, and for a few months in the north polar regions, the sun is always above the horizon and the day is twenty-four hours long. When the axis of the earth points away from the sun, the regions south of the equator enjoy spring and summer, and the south polar regions see the midnight sun. Thus, our seasons are produced. The sun rises in the east, and sets in the west, and appears directly overhead at noon only in midsummer at the equator. In midsummer at northern latitudes, it rises far to the north of east, and sets north of west; the sun is never directly overhead, but is toward the south, the angle depending on the seasons.

The hours of daylight and the seasons result from the angle of the axis of the earth, which remains constant as it makes its annual journey around the sun. The diagram shows the position of the rising sun with the different seasons, rising north of east in the summer, and south of east in the winter. The hours of daylight range from the summer maximum of about 15 hours about June 15 to a winter minimum of about 10½ hours about December 15 in the latitude of New York. Further north, the hours of daylight increase in summer to twenty-four hours at the North Pole. At the equator the hours of daylight remain relatively constant throughout the year.

The sun is a star, and not a very important one compared with many others. Its importance to us results from its relative nearness. Like all stars, the sun produces heat and light. The source of its energy is believed to be a form of atomic fission caused by the splitting of the hydrogen atom into helium. The atmosphere, which on earth protects us from the full intensity of solar radiation, is missing around the moon. This accounts for the clarity of the moon and our ability to see, with the naked eye, its mountains, plains, and valleys which we visualize as the "eyes and mouth" of the "man in the moon."

In 300 B.C., Aristarchus, an astronomer of the famed Alexandrian school, proposed a theory that the sun was the center of the universe; and as a reward, was punished as a heretic. If others had the same idea, they did not dare to propose it publicly again until A.D. 1543, when Copernicus published his monumental theory along the same lines. It was not until centuries later that the idea was accepted even by astronomers, and until comparatively recent years, the books of Copernicus were on the *Index* of the Catholic Church. It is through knowledge of the motions of the bodies of the solar system, the planets, the galaxies and their complicated mutual relationships, that modern timekeeping has been evolved. What we have learned has come from our earth-bound view. Conclusions have been based on what we have observed—the *apparent* movements of the heavenly bodies. In terms of precise measurement, the natural sun-earth-moon-star clock is not a simple timepiece, but an enormously complicated one with minute inaccuracies of undetermined causes.

The Celestial Sphere

When we look toward the heaven from some point where the view is unobstructed, we see what we call the sky. This is the celestial sphere which seems so real that it is often called the firmament. For convenience in describing the apparent positions of the stars, we must speak of the celestial sphere as though it really exists; the earth on which the observer stands appears to be some point located in the center of the sphere.

The figure shows the earth as the central point in the celestial sphere. The apparent path of the sun around the earth is called the ecliptic. The diagram also shows the celestial equator, which is a projection of the equator of the earth on the celestial sphere. The angle between the celestial equator and the ecliptic is 23° 27'. We have seen that the angle of the axis of the earth points alternately away from the sun and toward the sun. Obviously, there must be two points at

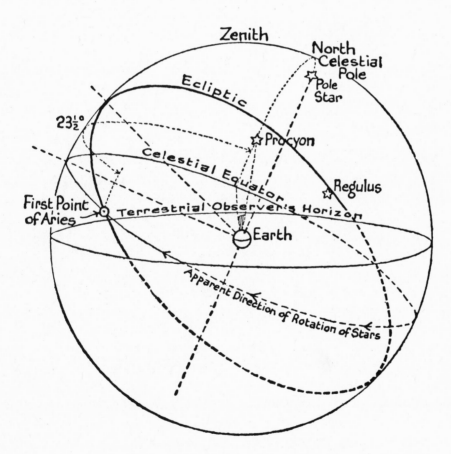

The earth and its relation to the celestial sphere.

which the axis of the earth is vertical with respect to the orbit of the sun, or the ecliptic. When at these two points, day and night are of equal length—the equinox. This happens in the spring at the vernal equinox, about March 21. At this time, in northern latitudes, the angle of the axis of the earth begins to turn toward the sun, the days begin to lengthen, and spring and summer soon follow. About September 21, at the autumnal equinox, the reverse takes place. Once again day and night are of equal length; but now, the axis of the earth begins to turn away from the sun; the days get shorter, and are soon followed by the chill of autumn and winter. Halfway between these two points comes, on one side, the shortest day of the year, about December 21, and the longest, about June 21. These points are called winter and summer solstices. The length of the four seasons are not precisely the same because the length of the days varies, as is explained later in discussing the equation of time. Calculated to the nearest hour, the length of each of the seasons north of the equator are:

Spring—vernal equinox to summer solstice	92 days,	23 hours
Summer—summer solstice to autumnal equinox	93 days,	13 hours
Autumn—autumnal equinox to winter solstice	89 days,	16 hours
Winter—winter solstice to vernal equinox	89 days,	1 hour

For the southern hemisphere, the same times prevail if we read summer for winter, and spring for autumn.

The Precession of the Equinoxes

The time between successive arrivals of the sun to the celestial equator, or the vernal equinox, determines the length of the tropical year, which is what is normally meant by the word year. Now enters the first of many complications in the celestial clock. The north polar axis of the earth, when projected to the celestial sphere, traces a circle very slowly, making one complete round in about 25,800 years. As a result, the time of the vernal equinox changes very slightly—about 50.3 seconds per year, or about 0.14 second daily. This is called *precession*.

The circle traced by the earth's polar axis, which causes precession, is not smooth, but consists of small waves due to nodding of the earth's axis. This is called *nutation*. The period of each complete wave is 19 years. The nod, at its maximum, is 9″ of angle. While precession and nutation are little but meaningless words to most of us, they are of enormous importance in astronomy and navigation. Most of us think of the North Star Polaris as indicating true north, while obviously, true north must vary through the movement of the axis of the earth. In the ephemeris of the navigator, true north is given for each month of each year by statement of the angles of certain fixed stars, such as Polaris to the true north. The circular motion of the *south* polar axis is the reverse of that of the north.

The Moon

The orbit of the moon is inclined by 5° to the apparent orbit of the sun. Since the moon completes its rotation around the earth in less than a month, half of this time it is above the celestial equator, and half below it. This causes the moon to rise and set a little later each day, the average delay being 51 minutes.

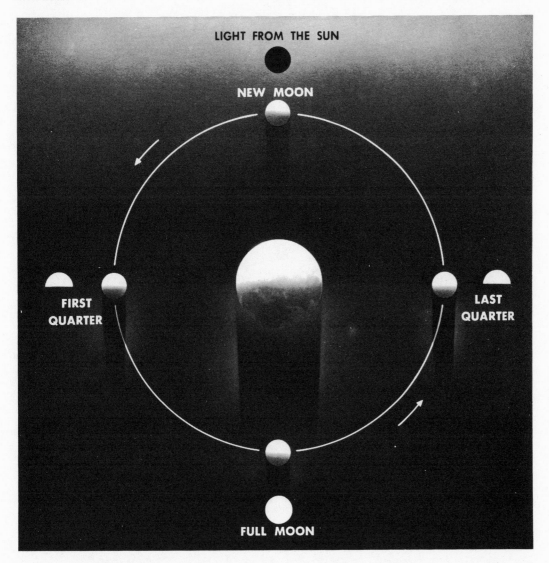

The phases of the moon and the rise and fall of tides follow the revolution of the moon around the earth. The moon completes its orbit with respect to its apparent position among the stars in about 27⅓ days. This is the sidereal month. Due to the fact that the earth rotates around the sun and carries the moon with it, the lunar cycle as we see it from earth is 2 days longer. The average time of a lunar cycle is 29.53059 days. The lunar calendars counted the month as 29 days.

The phases of the moon, which have excited the admiration of mankind from earliest days, are due to two circumstances: first, the moon shines only by reflected sunlight; and second, as it revolves around the earth, different portions of its sunlit side are presented to our view. When the sun is in back of the moon, so to speak, the moon receives no illumination which we can see, and is invisible to us. Technically, this is the phase of the new moon. Two or three days later, the moon moves slightly east of the sun, and becomes visible in the western sky soon after sunset. It appears to us as the beautiful crescent moon. The cusps, or horns, of the crescent moon are always turned away from the sun and, therefore, never point downward when the sun is below the horizon, although many artists are not acquainted with this simple fact. In northern latitudes, the horns of the young moon, when it is visible after sunset, are always turned upward and to the left. When the moon first comes out of its new moon phase, reflection from the earth partially illuminates that part which is turned away from the sun. We

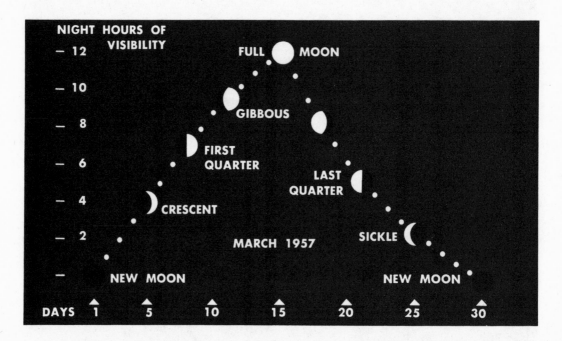

The Moon Clock. The moon is invisible when it is between us and the sun. This is called the new moon. The first thin crescent appears briefly close behind the setting sun near the horizon. The moon in its first quarter is first visible at the zenith at sunset. The full moon rises in the eastern sky as the sun is setting toward the west, reaches its highest point at midnight, and then sets in the west as the sun is rising. It is thus visible practically throughout the night. The moon in its last quarter rises at midnight and reaches its highest point at sunrise. The dying sickle moon rises with the first blush of dawn and shines briefly until the sun rises behind it. The chart shows the approximate hours of visibility of the moon during the month of March, 1957, when the complete cycle of its phases occurred within it.

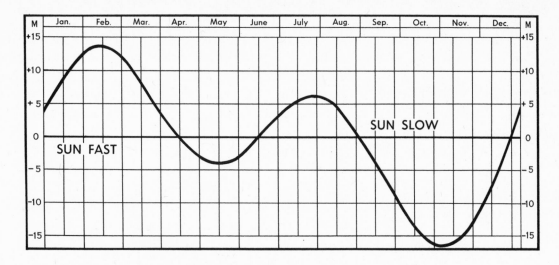

The Equation of Time. The sundial shows clock noon only four days of the year. The difference in time at various periods is known as the equation of time.

see an earthlit lunar landscape which is fancifully called "the old moon in the new moon's arms." As the crescent moon grows on succeeding nights, a full half of it becomes illuminated, and the moon appears as a semicircle. This phase is called the first quarter. Between the first quarter and the full moon, the moon is said to be gibbous. Following the full moon, the succession of phases is reversed, and we have the third quarter, and finally the sickle moon, preface to the "death" of the moon, from which the scythe of Father Time originated.

The phases of the moon do not appear to be precise quarters of its complete cycle, and appear to vary from 6 to 8 days. In one instance, the quarters seem to take 8–6–7–8 days; in another, 8–7–7–8 days. This apparent variation is due to the fact that the moon is visible only at night. If the moon were visible at all times, the cycles would be exactly the same length. Most calendars show the day on which the phases occur, and almanacs show the time to the hour.

The Equation of Time

The path of the earth around the sun is not a true circle, but an ellipse, and the earth moves more rapidly on some parts of its course than others. This difference in speed of travel causes shifts in the solar noon—the point at which the sun is at its highest, the zenith. It also causes the actual length of the day from noon to noon to change. The difference in the length of the day amounts, at its maximum, to about 16 minutes. This varies slightly from year to year. For navigational purposes, the exact time of solar noon must be known, and this is given for every day in the year in the almanacs and ephemerides published by the principal governments, such as the *American Ephemeris and Nautical Almanac*. This is called the equation of time.

Reference to establishing the length of the astronomical day from noon to noon is, of course, the procedure of astronomers, who count the day in that fashion. The civil day begins at midnight.

In early days, the error in timepieces was greater than the difference between the length of days, and clocks were usually set to time at the apparent noon, as indicated by a sundial. As timepieces improved, it was decided that the only way to reconcile matters was to average out the length of the days in the year and to assume that the actual differences did not exist.

The Mean Solar Day

The average length of the day is called the mean solar day. Our clocks and watches show divisions of the mean solar day. On October 21, 1884, at the International Prime Meridian Conference held in Washington, D.C., the mean solar day was put into effect as the universal day throughout the world. Perhaps this is the only international agreement that has ever been kept!

Sun time and clock time correspond only at four times of the year—at approximately December 25, April 16, June 15, and September 1. At about February 11, sun noon comes about 14 minutes, 28 seconds later than clock noon. At about November 3, sun noon is about 16 minutes, 21 seconds earlier than clock noon.

Sidereal Time

Before the days of telescopes, approximate time was determined by observation of the position of the sun by day, and the circumpolar stars by night; and to a lesser extent, of the moon and its relationship to the fixed stars. The relatively large size of the sun and its enormous luminosity make close time measurements impossible. The same difficulty arises in trying to make precise time calculations from observation of the moon. With relatively small magnification, however, the exact time the transit of a star passes a hairline in an exactly positioned telescope can be determined with great accuracy.

To keep our basic timepieces on time, the United States Naval Observatory observes some fifteen stars nightly, and establishes their time of transit with great accuracy. Some two hundred stars, known as Almanac Stars, are used for this purpose. The position at which these stars will be found at any time has been calculated through many thousands of observations. All stars move, although in some instances the movement is so slight that it might be imperceptible in a lifetime of observations. Some stars are moving westward, some northward, eastward, or southward; some away from us, and others toward us. Though the time error calculated from the apparent movement of a star might be as little as 0.0007 second nightly, all such errors must be taken into account. Over the years, the accuracy of the time of transit of stars has been improved.

At first, it was done by the eye-and-ear method, where the eye watched the star through a telescope, while the ear listened to the tick of the pendulum of a clock. Today, exact time of the transit of a star is determined by the United States Naval Observatory by means of what is called a photographic zenith tube. This is a low-power telescope permanently fixed to a point straight up, the zenith, with which is associated a camera with a motor drive to keep the star in focus during the required 20-second exposure. The photograph shows the passage of the star over a scale made of a series of hairlines. The exposure is begun precisely at the assumed time of transit according to the observatory clock. The position of the star on the scale in the photograph determines the error in the clock. Through a series of such observations made on clear nights, exact time is fixed by the Naval Observatory with an accuracy of about 0.003 second.

Due to the fact that as the earth revolves on its axis, it also rotates around the sun in the same direction, the apparent position of a star as recorded through a transit telescope, returns nightly in less time than the completion of the solar day. The time established by observation of the stars is called *sidereal* time, and is the "time" employed in astronomy and navigation. The sidereal day is shorter than the solar day by about 3 minutes, 55.909 seconds. In the course of a year, this adds up to about a full day. The sidereal year is thus 366 *sidereal* days. The actual length of the sidereal year is 365.25636 *mean solar* days, which is very slightly different from the length of the tropical year, counted from vernal equinox to vernal equinox, which has a length of 365.24219 mean solar days.

Standard Time

The rapid expansion of rail transportation in about 1860 produced a serious time problem. In the latitude of New York, for example, true time (sun time) changes about 1 minute for every 12½ miles of travel east or west. Around 1860, there were some 300 local times observed throughout the United States. Before 1883, the railroads had solved this problem by establishing what is known as railroad time. Trains were scheduled throughout the length of a line or division according to one time. For instance, the Pennsylvania Railroad in the East used Philadelphia time, which was 5 minutes slower than New York time and 5 minutes faster than Baltimore time. The Baltimore & Ohio used Baltimore, Columbus, Vincennes, New York, Philadelphia, and Chicago times, depending on the divisions. Altogether, there were some 100 different railroad times in use over the country. The railroads' problem is detailed in a pamphlet issued by the Association of American Railroads, called *The Day of Two Noons*.

As early as 1828, Sir John Herschel, the astronomer, had advocated standardization of time in England, and twenty years later, Greenwich time became

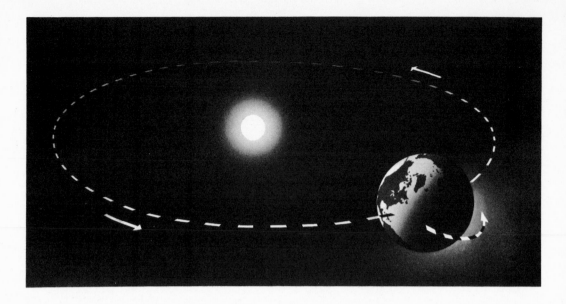

Our fundamental time standard is due to the counterclockwise revolution of the earth on its own axis, and to its yearly rotation around the sun in the same direction. The combination of these two motions makes the length of the sidereal day (measured by the apparent movement of the stars) 23 hours, 56 minutes, 4.9 seconds, and the sidereal year 366 sidereal days. Astronomical calculations and celestial navigation which are based on observation of the heavenly bodies are made according to sidereal time.

standard for all England, Scotland, and Wales. One of the earliest advocates of standard time in the United States was Professor Charles F. Dowd, who recommended that time be uniform in belts 15° wide, and that the United States be divided into 4 standard time zones.

This plan was proposed to the railroads in 1872, and adopted in 1883. The plan, worked out in co-operation with the Naval Observatory, ordered that the 75th, 90th, 105th, and 120th meridians would mark the approximate center of the 4 zones. Sunday was selected as the day to make the change because fewer trains would be running. At noon, November 18, 1883, taking the time by telegraph from the pendulum of the master clock at the United States Naval Observatory, all railroad clocks and watches were changed to the new time. This became known as "the day of two noons." In the eastern part of each zone, clocks had to be set back from 1 to 30 minutes, so there was another noon when railroad time went into effect. Western parts of each zone were "projected into the future"—as one newspaper commented, as much as 30 minutes. It was altogether an epic event, but although some protested the change as "against God's laws," the majority felt that it was a good step.

The problem was not unique to the United States, but world-wide. It was on the agenda of the Prime Meridian Conference of 1884, which made mean solar time universal throughout the world. At this conference, the whole world was divided into 24 time zones, each 15° of longitude wide. The center of the first zone was established at the longitude of the Greenwich Observatory, with the meridian identified as 0°. The zones east of Greenwich are numbered 1 to 12, with a prefix *minus* indicating the hours to be subtracted to obtain Greenwich time. The zones to the west are similarly numbered, but prefixed *plus*, showing the numbers to be added to get Greenwich time. The longitudinal position of any point on the globe can be identified as so many degrees and so many minutes east or west of Greenwich. The longitude of New York City is written as: 73° 59′ 31″ W. The length of a degree of longitude in miles on the earth's surface is not uniform, but varies with the latitude and gets smaller as one goes from the equator toward either pole. The length of a degree of longitude for various latitudes is:

DEGREE OF LATITUDE	STATUTE MILES
0°	69.172
10	68.129
20	65.026
30	59.956
40	53.063
50	44.552
60	34.674
70	23.729
80	12.051
90	0.

In this connection, it might be mentioned that a nautical mile is a measurement of 1′ of arc on the earth's surface, and it varies with the latitude. It is not a fixed linear measurement, as is the land mile. The length of a nautical mile at the equator is 6,046 feet, and varies from this to 6,108 feet at the poles. For practical purposes, a nautical mile is calculated as 6,080 feet, which still leaves the expression "knots per hour" as a somewhat meaningless phrase.

The international date line was placed at the 180th meridian on the opposite side of the world from Greenwich. Crossing the line in a westerly direction, as from San Francisco to Japan, one loses a day; in the reverse direction, a day is gained. Thus, if on a boat traveling from the Pacific Coast to the Orient, and one crossed the international date line at 12:00 noon on Wednesday, the next hour would be counted as 1:00 P.M. *Tuesday;* if at midnight Wednesday, it would be followed by 1:00 A.M. Wednesday, again. On a voyage from Hong Kong to San Francisco, if the date line were crossed at noon on Wednesday, the next hour would be counted as 1:00 P.M. *Thursday;* if at midnight, 1:00 A.M. would be Friday. With a map of the world, or a globe marked with the meridians, it is quite simple to calculate the time anywhere in the world by observing the rule that the time changes 1 hour for each 15° of longitude, though the international date line sometimes presents a problem that may require thoughtful concentration. Lines of the division of the various times are not straight lines. Where a city is close to the dividing line between one zone and another, it can make its choice as to which zone it will be. Thus, Cleveland, which properly should be in the Central time zone, has elected to be in the Eastern zone, and its clocks are set to the same time as New York City.

To facilitate the designation of zone time in coded messages, and for quick references, a system employing alphabetical suffixes is coming into wide usage for expressions of zone time. The 12 "plus zones" west of the Greenwich, or "0 (*Z*) zone," use the letters *N* through *Y*, consecutively; the 12 "minus zones," east of Greenwich, use the letters *A* through *M* (except *J*). The following table shows the time zones, descriptions, and suffixes:

ZONE	DESCRIPTION	SUFFIX	ZONE	DESCRIPTION	SUFFIX
$7\frac{1}{2}$° W. to $7\frac{1}{2}$° E.	0	Z	$7\frac{1}{2}$° W. to $22\frac{1}{2}$° W.	+ 1	N
$7\frac{1}{2}$° E. to $22\frac{1}{2}$° E.	− 1	A	$22\frac{1}{2}$° W. to $37\frac{1}{2}$° W.	+ 2	O
$22\frac{1}{2}$° E. to $37\frac{1}{2}$° E.	− 2	B	$37\frac{1}{2}$° W. to $52\frac{1}{2}$° W.	+ 3	P
$37\frac{1}{2}$° E. to $52\frac{1}{2}$° E.	− 3	C	$52\frac{1}{2}$° W. to $67\frac{1}{2}$° W.	+ 4	Q
$52\frac{1}{2}$° E. to $67\frac{1}{2}$° E.	− 4	D	$67\frac{1}{2}$° W. to $82\frac{1}{2}$° W.	+ 5	R
$67\frac{1}{2}$° E. to $82\frac{1}{2}$° E.	− 5	E	$82\frac{1}{2}$° W. to $97\frac{1}{2}$° W.	+ 6	S
$82\frac{1}{2}$° E. to $97\frac{1}{2}$° E.	− 6	F	$97\frac{1}{2}$° W. to $112\frac{1}{2}$° W.	+ 7	T
$97\frac{1}{2}$° E. to $112\frac{1}{2}$° E.	− 7	G	$112\frac{1}{2}$° W. to $127\frac{1}{2}$° W.	+ 8	U
$112\frac{1}{2}$° E. to $127\frac{1}{2}$° E.	− 8	H	$127\frac{1}{2}$° W. to $142\frac{1}{2}$° W.	+ 9	V
$127\frac{1}{2}$° E. to $142\frac{1}{2}$° E.	− 9	I	$142\frac{1}{2}$° W. to $157\frac{1}{2}$° W.	+10	W
$142\frac{1}{2}$° E. to $157\frac{1}{2}$° E.	−10	K	$157\frac{1}{2}$° W. to $172\frac{1}{2}$° W.	+11	X
$157\frac{1}{2}$° E. to $172\frac{1}{2}$° E.	−11	L	$172\frac{1}{2}$° W. to 180° W.	+12	Y
$172\frac{1}{2}$° E. to 180° E.	−12	M			

In this table, zones *R, S, T,* and *U* correspond, respectively, to Eastern, Central, Mountain, and Pacific zones in the United States.

The distance between degrees of longitude in the northern parts of the earth is so small that great difficulties were experienced with aerial navigation over the pole when following the usual navigational methods. At 30° north latitude, the length of a degree of longitude is less than half that at the equator, and rapidly reduces to 0° at the pole. In flying over the polar area, using ordinary charts, the navigator found that he had to change course by 1° every 4 minutes in a flight of some 10 hours, from Scandinavia to Alaska. To avoid this difficulty, a grid system has been devised, with parallel grids replacing the converging meridians beginning at about 60° north latitude. With this system, the navigator establishes his flight direction parallel to the master meridian of the grid, and flies in a straight line until he meets the beginning of the conventional meridian system on the opposite side of the world. This was one of the many difficulties which had to be cleared up before commercial airplane flights over the top of the world could be made a reality. While not distinctly a part of our subject, the problem of flying on the grid pattern was enormously complicated by the fact that the magnetic compass is completely unreliable in extreme northern areas, and both the gyrocompass and astrocompass must be used together, and direction checked by calculation every 20 minutes during

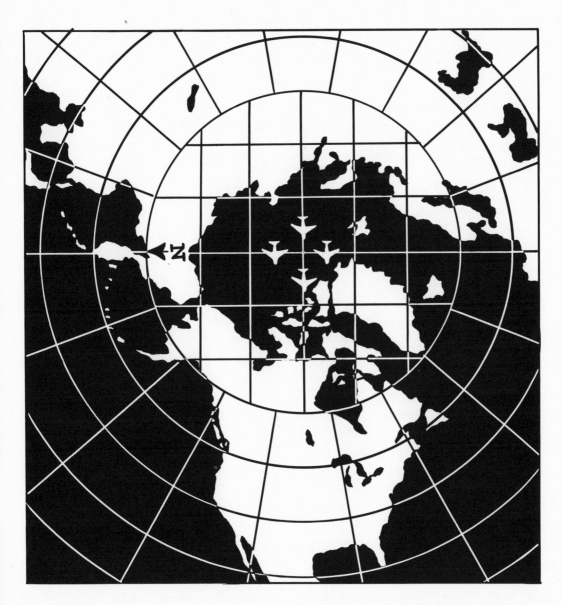

The grid system at the top of the world which replaces the meridians of longitude for air navigation.

the flight. However, the local time changes according to the old meridians, and on an across-the-pole flight one arrives in Fairbanks a half-hour before take-off time in Bardufoss.

Reports of the nightly observations from observatories of nations which are members of the International Astronomical Union are forwarded to the International Time Bureau in Paris, which is supported by the Union. The data from all is intercompared, but the calculations are of such magnitude that a year or more elapses before the correct determination of the length of each sidereal day is available. The probable error after all this is something between one and two milliseconds.

It may come as something of a shock to learn that no two clocks in the world keep *precisely* the same time, nor has any clock so far been made that will run with perfect accuracy indefinitely. Through the observations of our astronomers, the errors, however small in our present clocks, can be detected, and allowance made for them.

The location of the prime meridian at Greenwich was not agreed upon without discussion. Competition came from Russia. In 1833, Emperor Nicholas invited the German astronomer Frederich Wilhelm Struve to become the head of the Royal Observatory which was to be built near the village of Pulkovo, not far from the present Leningrad (then St. Petersburg). Its equipment was to be the finest in the world, with precision instruments which would surpass even those of Greenwich and the Paris observatories. Struve was considered one of the world's foremost astronomers, and was the author of several books which were considered milestones in astronomical history. He accepted the position, and the observatory began study of the fixed stars and precise determination of longitude. In this work, he employed as many as sixty-eight chronometers which were transported on many voyages across the Baltic and the North Sea to the Thames. With the work of Struve, the reputation of the Observatory of Pulkovo surpassed that of Greenwich, and there arose the problem of which observatory should win the honor of setting the location of the prime meridian. Struve, himself, decided the issue, taking the position that the historic importance of Greenwich as the first to devote itself to the study of longitude made it the logical choice; and so it was decided.

Daylight-Saving or Summer Time

Daylight-saving time might be said to be a feeble effort of man to lessen his slavery to the clock. Benjamin Franklin is said to have voiced the danger of regulating one's life according to a man-made timepiece rather than that of nature—the sun. He advocated setting clocks ahead during the summer months so that people would get up closer to sunrise, and so get their work done. It was introduced during World War I for another purpose—to save some of the fuel used to produce light. It has been perpetuated largely, not in the interest

Photographic zenith tube at United States Naval Observatory makes photographs of stars as they pass directly overhead. The image of the star is picked up from its reflection in a pan of mercury under the tube. Since the mercury is liquid, its mirror surface is always flat and level. At the top of the tube is an eight-inch lens which is focused on a light-sensitive photographic plate. In spite of the apparent movement of the star, it is kept in precise focus during the required 20-second exposure by a motor-driven tracking system. The tube is firmly anchored in position and cannot be moved. Two of these instruments are regularly used for time determination—the one illustrated, in Washington, and the other at Richmond, Florida.

of work, but of play, giving people working in offices and factories an extra hour of daylight for recreation. The system is far from universal and often confusing; such as, Denver on standard time and Los Angeles on daylight-saving time, thus destroying the normal difference between Mountain and Pacific time. But Denver has just as much right to cling to standard time as Los Angeles has to go on daylight-saving. The "double summer time" which is frequently established in England adds to the confusion.

24-Hour Time and the Military

The division of the whole day into two periods of 12 hours each makes it necessary to follow any hour with the suffix A.M. or P.M. to show whether the hour is *ante meridiem* (before noon), or *post meridiem* (after noon). In Europe, practically all trains and planes are scheduled on a 24-hour time basis. The hours before noon are numbered 1 to 12; after noon, 13 to 24. Twenty-four o'clock is midnight, the point at which one civil day ends and another begins. This system has been followed by the military in Europe for some time.

Shortly before the outbreak of World War II, the 24-hour time system was adopted by the United States military forces. However, in order to prevent confusion in written or oral communications, all time references are given in 4 figures. Thus, 1:00 o'clock is written 01:00, and spoken as 0 one hundred, the hundred indicating, in all cases, an even hour. Noon is read as 12:00. Minutes less than an hour are read in the usual way: 1:36 A.M. becomes 01:36, and is spoken as 0 one thirty-six. For their own dispatch work, overseas airlines generally employ the 24-hour day, even though in the United States the printed timetables still maintain the A.M. and P.M. system.

Military watches with the usual 12-hour dial are made with an inside track in a second color, such as red, giving the equivalent 13 to 24 hours. Some watches are available with the 24 hours in a single circle. The hour hand in these watches makes one revolution in 24 hours. In the watch of the size of a conventional wrist watch, the hours are necessarily much closer together than we are accustomed to see. Should the 24-hour system be generally adopted, however, 24-hour dial watches would be most desirable.

G.M.T. and Standard Time

Navigators' watches in planes, and chronometers on ships making overseas runs are set to Greenwich Observatory time. This is referred to as Greenwich mean time, and abbreviated as G.M.T. Local time is identified by the time zone, as E.S.T. for Eastern standard time.

CHAPTER V

The Birth of the Timepiece

The Dial of Ahaz

THERE OCCURS, in Chapter 20 of II Kings of the Old Testament, the story of the recovery from illness of King Hezekiah and the miracle of the prophet Isaiah, which is often quoted as the beginning history of the timepiece. As set down in the King James Version, it reads:

> 20:8. And Hezekiah said unto Isaiah, What shall be the sign that the Lord will heal me, and that I shall go up into the house of the Lord the third day?
>
> 9. And Isaiah said, This sign shalt thou have of the Lord, that the Lord will do the thing that he hath spoken: shall the shadow go forward ten degrees, or back ten degrees?
>
> 10. And Hezekiah answered, It is a light thing for the shadow to go down ten degrees: nay, but let the shadow return backward ten degrees.
>
> 11. And Isaiah the prophet cried unto the Lord: and he brought the shadow ten degrees backward, by which it had gone down in the dial of Ahaz.

Ahaz was King of Judah, and the father of Hezekiah. The home of Hezekiah was Jerusalem, and the date of this event, about 700 B.C. Modern astronomy has calculated that a solar eclipse occurred in 689 B.C. which was visible in Jerusalem, and this could account for the miracle recorded. Just what the appearance of the dial of Ahaz was, we do not know. In other translations of the Bible, the word "degrees" is replaced with "steps." From contact with the Egyptians, the Jews would have known of the Egyptian obelisks.

These tapering, quadrangular shafts, often graven with hieroglyphics, some over a hundred feet in height, were symbols of the sun god Ra. The earliest known was erected around 2000 B.C. One of these, popularly known as Cleopatra's Needle, and presented by the khedive of Egypt to the City of New York in 1880, is a feature of Central Park. Another is in Trafalgar Square in London, and a third is placed in the center of the Place de la Concorde in Paris. Several were brought from Egypt and erected in Rome. The Egyptian priests termed the obelisk "the finger of God." The Greeks called such an upright structure a *gnomon,* meaning "one who knows," the name which we now give to the upright, shadow-casting part of a sundial. The Romans who brought obelisks home thought they were part of a sundial to mark hours. They were, rather, solar calendars intimately necessary to the worship of the sun, as we have already seen. Some obelisks were mounted on flights of steps, along which the shadow fell, and by its position gave the date for various festivals. The dial of Ahaz may have been an obelisk, or the vertical stick of the Greeks, which was similar. While it has been stated that the art of making sundials was known in ancient Babylonia, there is no clear evidence that this is true.

The hemicyclium, the earliest known sundial, excavated in Egypt but marked with Greek characters.

Origin of the Sundial

The earliest known form of ancient sundial was discovered in 1852, buried at the foot of an Egyptian obelisk, but its exact date is not known. This Egyptian sundial was made in a section of a concave cone, on which hour divisions were marked. It is believed to have had a single vertical post to cast the shadow. This form of sundial is called a hemicyclium. The fact that this Egyptian sundial was marked with Greek letters suggests that it was made close to the beginning of our era. The divisions of its dial were equally spaced, and the hours marked by the shadow would have been of unequal length. A frequently quoted authority as to the first sundial is the statement in Book II of Pliny's *Natural History,* which was written around A.D. 60: "The theory of the shadows and the science of gnomonics was discovered by Animaximenes, the pupil of Anaximander; he first exhibited at Sparta the timepiece they call Hunt-the-Shadow." This was around the sixth century B.C. It is not reasonable to believe that sundials indicating true hours appeared much before A.D. 1500. One of the earliest now in existence is on the Cathedral of Notre Dame at Chartres in northern France, and is dated 1578.

Before this time, sundials were not marked with hours. Reference has been made to the sundial in the Kirkdale Church in Yorkshire, which was marked with tides. Sundials marked with five divisions, which were called Mass clocks, were frequently set up in churchyards.

In the sixteenth and seventeenth centuries, "the science of dialing" received much attention. Pocket sundials were made in several forms. Some were fashioned of silver. A common form was known as the ivory book. This consisted of two tablets hinged together so that when opened, one was vertical and the other horizontal. They were connected by a string which acted as the gnomon.

The construction of an accurate sundial requires a knowledge of astronomy, geography, mathematics, and mechanics not known in early days. The whole dial must be constructed for the latitude of the place where it is to be used. The dial must be situated so that the gnomon, which casts the shadow, faces due north. The base must be horizontal. The angle of the gnomon should be such that along its length it will point in the direction of the northern pole of the earth's axis; i.e., approximately the polestar. Laying out the dial lines accurately presents an interesting problem of trigonometry.

The various dial lines do not make the same angle with each other. The location of the dial lines is different for dials used in different latitudes. Today, sundials are sold with the angle of the gnomon correct for the latitude of the place, but on a standard base with lines constructed for average latitude. The result may be an error of several minutes in each hour—perhaps of no particular consequence.

The sundial has obvious disadvantages as a timepiece which make its use limited. The movement of the shadow is so slow that it is useless to calculate minutes, and hopeless for an estimate of seconds. The oft-met inscription on sundials, "I count only the sunny hours," points to its greatest disadvantage. When the sun is obscured there is no shadow, and no time. The equation of time, which led to the adoption of mean solar time, also shows that the sundial indicates true noon only at four times during the year, and at other times can be as much as sixteen minutes off. Nevertheless, sundials were used for the setting of clocks, and even for establishing railroad time, within the last century.

The Water Clock or Clepsydra

Again according to Pliny, around 150 B.C. the sundial was abandoned as the official timepiece by Roman law, and the water clock (clepsydra) took its place. At this time, day and night were given equal length of twelve hours each.

The word clepsydra comes from two Greek words meaning "to steal water." In its simplest form, it consisted of a transparent vase, marked with lines or graduations, which was filled with water and emptied drop by drop through a small hole. The passage of the hours was read as the level of the water

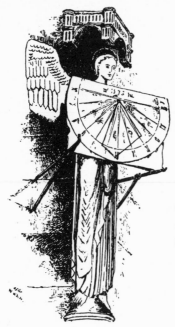

Sundial on Cathedral of Notre Dame in Chartres, France. The angel was erected in the twelfth century; the dial was added in the sixteenth century.

A Window Sundial of Stained Glass. This is an idea worthy of modern adaptation. A colorful dial could be painted on the glass. The gnomon would be mounted outside on the frame of the window. Unlike the usual sundial, the shadow would move like the hands of a clock when viewed from within.

Portable sundial with compass.

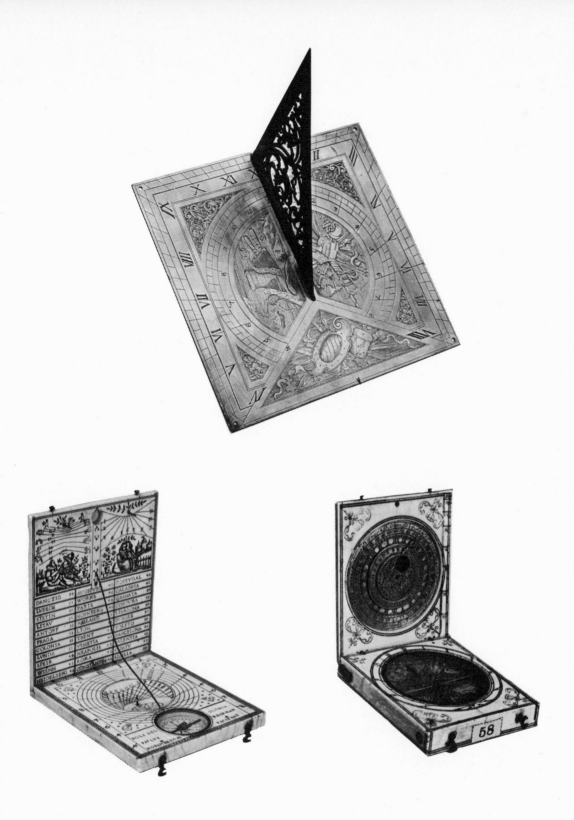

Sundials. (top) *Beautifully carved brass dial from garden sundial. Probably French. Eighteenth century.* (lower left) *An ivory book, pocket compass, and sundial made by Paulud Reinman (1578–1607), Nuremberg.* (lower right) *French version of the ivory-book type of sundial with compass. Seventeenth century.*

reached one graduation after another. Clepsydras of this simple form were used in the Roman senate to limit the time of speakers, the upper vase being made to hold a small amount of water. If the speaker was boring or talking out of turn, the senators would shout that his water should be taken away. If he was talking to the point, and ran out of time, they would petition the "chair" that more water should be allowed.

The immediate advantage of the clepsydra lay in its independence from the sun. It could tell time on cloudy days and at night. And, unlike the sundial, with simple precautions it would operate correctly wherever it was placed, and to that degree was portable. When perfected, it counted not only accurate minutes, but seconds as well, and so became a tool for precise astronomical observations. Simple water clocks were used in India and China as early as 4000 B.C.

It was found that the water dripped faster when the upper container was full than when partly empty, due to the pressure of the water. To overcome the difference in the rate of flow due to pressure, the upper chamber was kept filled continuously from a reservoir, so that the water level remained at approximately the same height. In this form, the time was read as the water rose in the lower vessel.

About 250 B.C., Archimedes developed the geared wheel, among other inventions. He is supposed to have applied gearing to the design of a water clock

Clepsydra of the eighteenth century. The advantage of the clepsydra lies in its independence from the sun.

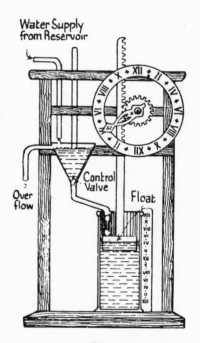

Gearing was applied to the water clock to move a hand, and later to effect various mechanical motions.

at about that time. Gearing of the most complicated kind, with levers and cams, and other devices to produce mechanical motion, was eventually introduced into the water clock. It was made to move a hand over dials, to strike bells, to run calendars, and to drive astronomical clocks for demonstrating the motion of the planets. In later years, many patents were taken out in connection with water clocks, some as late as the eighteenth century. The fact frequently over-looked in describing water clocks is that their accuracy is *basically* influenced only by atmospheric pressure and temperature—the same things which plague the best timepieces of today.

Until the perfection of the pendulum clock around 1700, the water clock was the most accurate of the world's timepieces. It was the servant of the great astronomers. The water clock was *King of Time* for over a thousand years, from the time of Julius Caesar to Louis XIV.

The water clock is gone, but it made a great contribution to later clocks and watches: the development of the gear work. The modern watchmaker can give thanks to the hundreds of unknown and unsung geniuses who, in making water clocks perform many functions, developed the rudimentary science of clock-works.

The history of timekeeping cannot be read without reference to general history. In the development of timekeeping, all of the sciences were involved; in particular, astronomy and mathematics. In the creation of timepieces, there must be a need and someone to pay the workman for his work. There must also exist a respect for learning and the learned. Such conditions existed in the period of the glory of Greece, when great progress was made in astronomy. One of the last of the great Greek scholars and natural scientists was Hipparchus, who founded an observatory at Alexandria, and discovered precession, an important contribution to timekeeping, in 180 B.C. Perhaps the very last was Claudius Ptolemaeus, usually known as Ptolemy, who in 150 B.C. wrote the *Almagest*, the great book which brought together all that was then known about astronomy.

With its preoccupation with war and conquest, Rome contributed little to the advancement of the basic natural sciences. By the third century A.D., Rome controlled all the countries on the shores of the Mediterranean, and almost all of Europe including Britain. Through the twin capitals of Rome and Constantinople, an active trade between East and West supported an increasing standard of living, and maintained many thriving cities. The gradual decay of this great empire has been recorded from a hundred points of view. Continuous pressure from the barbarians from the north led to a gradual emergence of the East as the center of culture and wealth; and in the fifth century, to the final collapse of the empire. This, alone, was not the cause of the dark ages into which Europe deteriorated. The *coup de grâce* was initiated by the birth of Mohammed, son of Abdullah, a merchant in Mecca in Arabia, and the founder of the Mohammedan religion Islam.

Even before the death of Mohammed in A.D. 632, the march of Islam began. In the next two hundred years, it had conquered the Persian Empire, Egypt, Syria, Africa, and penetrated into China and India. It overran Spain, the coast of Africa, of Italy, and of France; and Islam became master of the *mare nostrum,* the once Roman "lake." Without trade and commerce, all Europe withered. The open cities disappeared. In their stead came small walled cities—duchies, baronies, and bishoprics. Elsewhere was anarchy peopled with roving bandits. This was medieval Europe.

In 1453, Islam captured Constantinople, but the high point of its tide of conquest had been reached, and slowly started to recede. As with Rome and many before her, so it was with Islam and those who have since waged wars—in the long run, the winner loses; the champion, worn out by battles, eventually loses his crown.

The Science of the East

While scientific progress stopped in Europe, it was actively fostered in the great new empire being assembled by the victories of the soldiers of Allah. Bagdad, now the capital city of Iraq, in A.D. 800 was a metropolis of great magnificence, with over two million inhabitants, and the center of culture and learning of the Western world. Manuscripts and books of the Greek philosophers, geographers, astronomers, captured with the cities, were carried to Bagdad and translated into Arabic, the sacred language of the Koran. Among these was the *Almagest* of Ptolemy. Much of the learning of the ancient days was only preserved through Arabic translations. The *Almagest* was translated from Arabic into Latin between 1230 and 1496. What we call Arabic numerals originated in India, and were put to use in Arabia around A.D. 800. Roman figures made mathematical calculations a ponderous chore. With the magic Arabic numerals—one to nine plus a zero—solution of the most complicated mathematical problems was greatly simplified. Under the caliph, Harun al-Rashid, observatories were built in Bagdad and Damascus, and the study of astronomy as a science was actively undertaken. Water clocks with the most complicated actions and improved gear forms were developed.

One of these, presented in the year 800 by Harun al-Rashid to Charlemagne, in celebration of his coronation by Pope Leo III as Charles I, Emperor of the West, has been pictured from its description:

> The dial was composed of twelve small doors, which represented the hours; each door opened at the hour it was intended to represent, and out of it came the same number of little balls, which fell one by one, at equal intervals of time, on a bass drum. It might be told by the eye what the hour was by the number of doors that were open, and by the ear by the number of balls that fell. When it was twelve o'clock, twelve horsemen, in miniature, issued forth at the same time, and shut all the doors. (From Willis I. Milham, *Time and Timekeepers.*)

How the balls were returned to their places is not told, but probably this chore was the responsibility of the "keeper of the clock."

Virtually unknown to European countries, greater progress was made in the sciences in remote Arabia between 800 and 900 than for a thousand years before. Jewish scholars had an important role in the universities of Bagdad, and later carried Eastern culture into Europe.

Gerbert and the Escapement

The first European astronomer of note to emerge since the beginning of the Christian Era was Gerbert, a Benedictine monk, who was born around 920. He studied under Hatto, Archbishop of Vich, in Catalonia, where he came in contact with Eastern knowledge. He later lectured at the University at Reims, and here introduced the Arabic numerals into mathematical studies. (Arabic numerals were not used in England until some four hundred years later.) He constructed terrestrial and celestial globes to illustrate his lectures. Gerbert is credited with the first of a long series of inventions which were necessary in order to make an accurate mechanical timepiece—the *escapement*. He later became Pope Sylvester II, where his vast knowledge gave him the stature of a magician.

The city-state republics of Venice and Florence seem to have initiated a new and better Europe. By the thirteenth century, Venice had developed an enormous trade between the East and West, and with its acquired wealth, extended encouragement to the sciences as well as the arts. The Venetians brought Eastern alchemists, astronomers, and mathematicians into Europe. The Republic of Florence made parallel progress, particularly under the rule of the Medici family, which began in 1378. The Medicis maintained close relations with Venice, were friendly with the Arabians, and acquired great wealth with banking houses all over Europe. This environment, which fostered the art of Michelangelo and Cellini, gave the world the second of the new European astronomers: Toscanelli, a native of Florence.

In Florence was the beautiful *duomo,* cathedral church of Santa Maria del Fiore, a vast structure of superb design, which was begun in the year 1298, and not completed until the middle of the seventeenth century. Its dome, greatest among all the churches of the world, rises majestically to a height of three hundred feet above the marble pavement. Toscanelli arranged to have a small hole made in the very summit of the dome, and through this hole he was able to watch the movement of a star as it came into view and disappeared. It was the first transit "telescope," and forecast the method used by modern astronomers to tell time by the stars. By tracing the movement of sunlight projected on the floor through the same hole, Toscanelli made other useful astronomical calculations.

The escapement invented by Gerbert was not used to make a timepiece, but

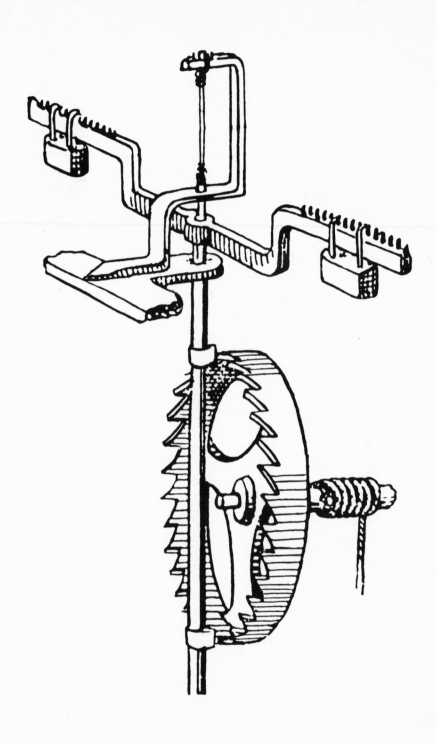

The primitive escapement with its foliot and balance.

The first mechanical timepiece which had no dial, no hands—just tolling bells to mark the time.

to operate a semiautomatic bell ringer. It had gears, and was powered with weights. The word clock was evolved from the Latin *clocca*, which means bell. The French word *cloche,* derived from the same source, meant both a clock as a timepiece and bell until the invention of the pendulum. After that, the clock-timepiece became *pendule.* The bell ringer of Gerbert was probably manually started.

The Foliot, the First Controller

The first *controller* to restrain uniformly the fall of the weights of the clockwork was called a *foliot.* It was a horizontal bar centered on a vertical rod, on which it could rotate freely. On the ends of the horizontal bar were notches on which hung movable weights. It was, in effect, a balance. Its vertical shaft had two protruding plates which engaged with the teeth of the escape wheel, which resembled a crown. The escapement was alternately locked and unlocked, and the power of the weight was released one tooth at a time, through the escape wheel. This made possible an automatic bell ringer. The first "clock" of Saint Paul's Cathedral in London, built around 1286, was a bell ringer. Around 1370, at Dijon, there was a decorative bell ringer with figures of a man and woman, which rotated and struck a bell with hammers held in their hands. Several bell ringers with male "Jacks" to strike the bell, were also erected in various places in England. A beautiful reproduction of an ancient bell ringer, which was originally placed on the New York Herald Building, is now erected in Herald Square in New York City. The beautifully balanced bronze jacks swing their hammers alternately to strike each hour on a bronze bell of singular musical quality. (Actually, the bell is struck from within by an electrical arrangement.)

The next addition was the dial, and just as the first automobile imitated the horse-drawn carriage, even to the whip socket, the first clocks with dials were made in imitation of a sundial. The dial, with twelve equal divisions, rotated under a slanting gnomon which served to mark the hour. Still later, the dial was fixed, and a single hand turned above it. One of the first monumental mechanical clocks was erected on the Royal Palace in Paris for Charles V of France in 1360. Monumental clocks such as this were the work of armorers or blacksmiths. That smaller clocks of finer workmanship were made by locksmiths, goldsmiths, or jewelers at an earlier period is illustrated by a manuscript in the Library of St. Marks in Venice, which describes in great detail a most complicated astronomical clock made by Giovanni de Dondi, a physician and astronomer, around 1370. Dondi was a product of the scientific renaissance of the Republic of Florence. Italian scholars claim that the first of all clock-watches were made in Padua, Venice, and Florence.

Peter Henlein and the Mainspring

Some time before 1500, miniature cathedral clocks, the first household clocks, made their appearance. About this time, the coiled spring, as a substitute for the weight as power, was introduced, it is said, by Peter Henlein of Nuremberg. This we know today as the *mainspring*. This led to smaller, or table clocks, and then to clock-watches, and finally to watches.

All of these early timepieces, clocks and watches, had two things in common: they all struck bells, and they didn't keep good time. A clock or watch that was not off more than two hours a day was good.

It might be mentioned here that the sandglass was the first seen in Europe in the eighth century. During the period we have just been discussing, it was widely used; but most of the prized antique sandglasses of the museums were made after 1500.

CHAPTER VI

The Voyages of Exploration

Marco Polo and the Gold of the East

THE MARINE CHRONOMETER, the first accurate portable timepiece, was born of growing necessity, and was the product of a unique and important period in history, in which the great voyages of exploration took place. A pot of gold, in the form of the treasures of the East, was the lure that fired the spirit of adventure. These fabled lands were touched upon by legends of Alexander the Great. Missionaries had penetrated to the borders of Tibet, and brought back tales of Cathay. Then, through *The Book of Marco Polo,* came a great awakening. In November, 1271, Marco Polo, when a lad of seventeen, in the company of his father and uncle, left Acre, a seaport town in Syria, where they had an audience with the Pope. Proceeding overland, they reached northern China after an adventurous journey that covered almost three years. In 1295, the travelers returned to their home in Venice. There, Marco Polo became a captain of a war galleon of Venice, and by great good fortune, as it later developed, was captured in a battle between the Venetians and Genoese, and imprisoned in Genoa. In the years of his imprisonment, he dictated the stories of his travels.

Marco Polo's narrative gave to Europe its first knowledge of the vast size and wealth of China with its great cities; of strange Tibet with its lamaseries; of Burma, land of golden pagodas; of Siam, Cochin, Sumatra; of the island of Ceylon and its spices; of India, rich with gold, diamonds, and rubies; and of Japan, or Zipangu, a land of fabulous wealth toward which Columbus was to direct his ships. As Marco Polo describes it:

> I will tell you a wonderful thing about the Palace of the Lord of that Island. You must know that he hath a great palace which is entirely roofed with fine gold, just as our churches are roofed with lead, insomuch that it would be scarcely possible to estimate its value. Moreover, all the pavement of the Palace, and the floors of its chambers, are entirely of gold, in plates like slabs of stone, a good two fingers thick; and the windows also are of gold, so that altogether the richness of this Palace is past all bounds and belief. (From *The Book of Marco Polo.*)

Marco Polo's narrative, circulated through manuscripts in Latin and French throughout Europe, aroused both disbelief and amazement, although it was to prove substantially factual. Incidentally, the Arabian explorers and missionaries had traveled these regions around 900, but this was unknown to Europe.

Sir John Mandeville

More fire was added to the growing interest in the riches of the East by *The Voiage and Travaile of Sir John Maundevile, Kt.*, a strange narrative of fancy, fable, and fact, which purported to describe the wanderings of this illustrious knight, which began in 1322 and covered thirty-four years. Of this book it is said that more copies were made in manuscript form in the late fourteenth and fifteenth centuries than any other book, except the Bible. The East was a land of *"fyn Gold, precyous Stones and grete Perles." The Voyage of Sir John Mandeville,* as it was called in later years, was probably the most widely read adventure book of all times.

The world in the days of Columbus was pictured on maps as a great land mass surrounded by ocean, the center of the world being Jerusalem. Roughly, it was a circle divided by a *T* into three parts. The largest part over the top of the *T* was Asia; the other two-thirds of the *T* were given to Europe and Africa. Transferred to a globe, there was merely an expanse of ocean between Europe and the eastern coast of Asia and the riches of Zipangu, which had first been described by Marco Polo.

The rise of Portugal as a sea power, under Prince Henry the Navigator (1394–1460), was largely the result of voyages of exploration which he encouraged. His captains discovered the Azores and Cape Verde Islands; they sailed ever further down the coast of Africa, and by 1486, had reached the Cape of Good Hope, the tip of that continent.

The navigational tools available to the Portugese sailors and to Columbus were meager indeed. The idea of using natural magnetic iron (loadstone) to magnetize a steel needle, which led to the invention of the compass, is credited to Flavio Gioja of Amalfi early in the fourteenth century. The only other navigational instrument was the *astrolabe,* which consisted of a circular plate divided into degrees with a rotatable pointed pivot at its center, by which the angle between two stars, or the altitude of a star from the horizon, could be crudely determined. A variation of the astrolabe was the *cross staff.* With the compass, the navigator could set a course. With the astrolabe, he could roughly determine latitude, or his position north and south. By observation of the position of the circumpolar stars at night, or of the sun by day, he could determine local time.

The achievements of the Portugese navigators and the stories of the riches of the East, seemingly just waiting to be taken, spread to Spain, France, England, and the Netherlands, which at this time were the only countries beside

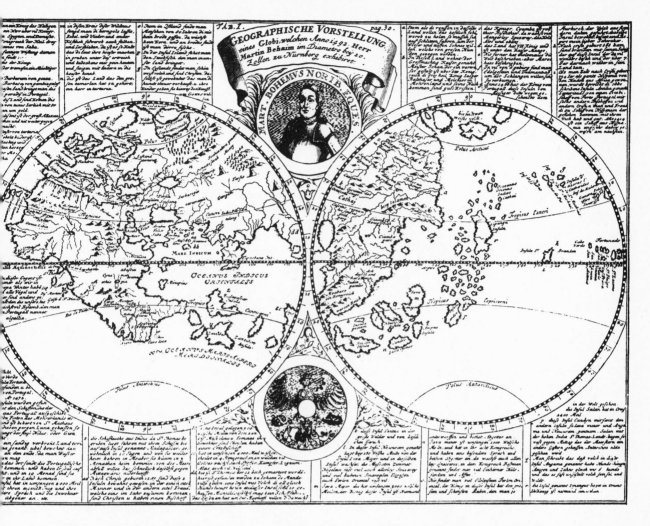

The World of Columbus. Only the Atlantic Ocean separated Europe from Asia and the riches of Zipangu. The drawing is from Martin Behaim's globe presented to the city of Nuremberg in 1492, and is the oldest known globe which has been preserved.

The forerunner of the sextant was the astrolabe, the single astronomical instrument of the days of Columbus.

Harrison's Chronometer No. 1. The first "time machine" created by John Harrison designed to give the longitude by "keeping" the time prevailing at the port of departure during a sea voyage. It was an amazing creation of a man without scientific training, and was invented, so to speak, piece by piece as its construction was carried out over a period of six years. All of the gears are of wood except the escape wheel, which is brass. The teeth of the pinions are lignum vitae, one of the hardest of woods. It has a grasshopper escapement of original design with wooden pallets. Two ponderous balance wheels weighing 5 pounds each are controlled by four balance springs. The base measures 2 by 1½ feet. The whole machine weighs 75 pounds. The four dials in the front record seconds at the top; below this, minutes and hours; at the bottom, days. It kept better time than previous "portable" timepieces, but was rejected because of impossibility of duplication.

A modern ship's chronometer.

Portugal to have relatively strong central governments. Soon ship captains and adventurers were knocking at royal doors, seeking backing for voyages of exploration. One of these was Columbus, and the story of how Isabella offered her jewels to finance his plan is a romantic episode of treasured memory from our schoolbooks.

The Error of Columbus

The theory of Columbus was that 225° of the earth's area was known to the ancients. With the discovery of the Azores and Cape Verde Islands by the Portugese, another 15° had been made known. With estimates that had been made of the size of Asia, he figured that it filled much of the unknown 120°, and that the shores of Zipangu lay but a short sail away to the west. This was not an idle guess. He was an able commander, a skilled navigator, and had made a great study of geography. He consulted the great astronomer Paolo Toscanelli of Florence who, it is believed, had made an intense study of the manuscripts of Marco Polo. Toscanelli not only concurred with Columbus, but furnished him with a map and a suggested course.

The story of the voyages of Columbus, Cabot, Amerigo Vespucci, and the others, need be recalled only in that *the names of their discoveries were added to the map on the coast of Asia, including Bachaloas (Newfoundland), Florida, and Mexico!* In 1521, Magellan sailed down the coast of South America through the straight which now bears his name, crossed the Pacific to the Philippines, sailed around

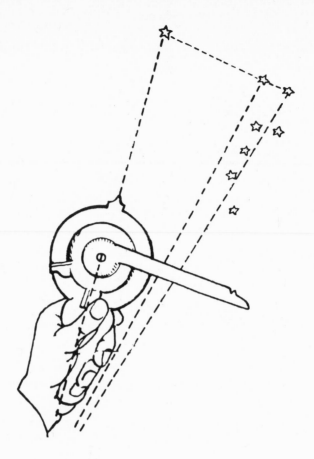

The Nocturnal, an ancient navigational instrument believed to have been invented in the sixteenth century. By sighting the polestar through the center hole, and moving the long arm until it was parallel with the pointers of the Big Dipper, the hour in sidereal time could be read on a 24-hour scale which was on the opposite side of the instrument as illustrated. By means of the small arm, which could be set to the month and day, using tables prepared for the purpose, the sidereal time of observation was converted into solar time with an accuracy of about 15 minutes. Since the approximate hour of midnight could be fixed with the Nocturnal, latitude could be found as with observation of the sun at noon. Some Nocturnals were extremely complex. They were not used as navigational instruments after about 1700.

Java and across the Indian Ocean to the Cape of Good Hope, and thence up the coast of Africa and home, without touching Asia. Then, in 1499, after a voyage of twenty-six months, Vasco da Gama, the Portugese navigator, returned home after reaching Calcutta in India, by sailing down the west coast of Africa and around the Cape of Good Hope, and thence up the east coast and across the Arabian Sea. Geographers were thrown into the greatest confusion. It was not until the map of Mercator, in 1577, that some approximation of the position of the American continent was recorded.

The immediate cause of the error of Columbus was the small size of the earth according to the estimate which he followed. Around 200 B.C., Eratosthenes made an estimate of the length of a degree of longitude as 59½ miles. While this fact was known to Columbus, he believed that the figure of 56⅔ miles, estimated by the Moslem geographer Alfraganus, was more correct; but he made the disastrous mistake of interpreting the length of the *miles* according to the Roman measure of 1,480 meters. Had he calculated in *Arabic* miles, a degree would have worked out to 62 of our nautical miles. According to Columbus, a degree measured only 45 of our nautical miles. In addition, he accepted Marco Polo's idea that Japan lay 1,500 miles off the China Coast, and he also increased the estimate of the size of the land mass of Asia. The final figure of the distance to be sailed from the Canary Islands to Zipangu and its gold worked out to 2,400 of our nautical miles. The actual air-mile distance is 10,600 nautical miles! In 1671, the French astronomer Picard figured the length of a degree of longitude as 61 miles for the latitude of Paris, which is close to the figure used today. But it still did not solve the problem of determining on *which* longitude a ship happened to be on the trackless ocean.

The Problem of Longitude

The importance of this problem led to the posting of magnificent cash awards for its solution. In 1604, Philip III of Spain put up 10,000 ducats; Holland followed with a prize of 25,000 florins; Louis XIV of France posted 100,000 florins. These prizes totaled well over $1,000,000, in terms of today's money. But there were no claimants.

As early as 1450 astronomers had suggested that longitude could be determined by the angle of the fixed stars to the moon; but the star tables then available were inadequate to make the method practical. In 1675, Charles II of England ordered the building of the Greenwich Observatory to create the star tables to determine longitude by the method of lunar distances, as Werner and others had suggested. The preparation of the first *Nautical Almanac* giving some of the essential information required a hundred years.

Galileo, who with his telescope had discovered five of the satellites, or moons, of Jupiter, suggested that longitude could be found through their varying periods of revolution. On a tossing ship, however, such observations were impossible. As a young man, Galileo had discovered the principle of the pendulum, but not until fifty years later did he think of applying it to a clock. He left a plan for such a pendulum clock to his son, with the thought that if time could be *carried* by means of an accurate pendulum clock, the problem of longitude could be readily solved. The clock was never made, but the idea was found impractical when Christian Huygens actually constructed a pendulum clock and tried it out on shipboard. However, the idea of using a timepiece to determine longitude had been born.

$1,000,000 for a Timepiece

With the passage of a full century after the posting of the first award by Philip III of Spain, the problem of finding longitude was as far from being solved as ever. In 1710, a great number of English sea captains, and others, petitioned the House of Commons for action. The loss of ships, men, cargo, and treasure had been mounting as ocean commerce had grown during the period of the colonization of the New World, and the expanding trade between the mother countries and their colonies. After long debate, the House of Commons, in 1714, passed a bill "for providing a publick reward for such person or persons as shall discover the Longitude." The bill authorized the payment of £10,000 if longitude could be determined within 1°; £15,000, if within 40″ of arc; £20,000, if within 30″—in nautical miles, about 60 miles, 40 miles, and 30 miles.

The prize was won by John Harrison, who was born in Yorkshire, England, in 1693. The son of a carpenter, he learned the trade of his father, but in early years displayed a keen understanding of mechanics, and constructed a clock with gears made of wood. When he was twenty-two, he had built the first of several grandfather clocks. While working on these, he made two important inventions: a compensation pendulum, and a new form of escapement with which he made several clocks of great accuracy. One of these did not vary a second a month during a period of fourteen years. Somewhere along the line he heard about the prize offered by the Board of Longitude, and decided to try for it.

In 1728, he came to London with drawings of a proposed timepiece, and managed to meet George Graham, a famous English clockmaker, who was so impressed with the design that he loaned Harrison a sum of money to help him make it, and encouraged him to complete it and have it tested. Harrison returned to his home, which was then in Barrow-on-Humber in Lincolnshire. The completion of the first timepiece required six years. The gears were made of wood; the case measured 2 by 1½ feet; and the whole machine weighed 75 pounds. On a voyage to Lisbon, ordered by the Board of Longitude, it behaved well, but was not sufficiently accurate to win a prize. The Board, however, voted him £500 to continue his work. In 1739, he completed No. 2, which was along the lines of the first, but was not tested because England was at that time at war with Spain. In 1740, he began No. 3, on which he spent seventeen years. During this period, the Board voted him five payments of £500 each. No. 3 was again not sufficiently accurate, although much improved, and he began work on No. 4. The first three were all large, heavy, boxlike affairs. No. 4 was the size of a large watch.

The testing of Harrison's No. 4 was in charge of Nevil Maskelyne, Astronomer Royal of Greenwich Observatory, who had already proposed to the Royal Navy that the best method of determining longitude was to measure, with the sextant, the angle of known stars to the moon, using the tables prepared by the Observatory, on which Maskelyne had devoted so much time. Harrison's timepiece was placed aboard the ship *Depworth*, which, leaving Spithead, touched at Portland and Plymouth, and then set sail for Madeira. The timepiece was placed in the care of four persons, each with a separate key, and all four had to be present to unlock the case at each winding. With the sighting of Madeira, it was found that calculations of the longitude with Harrison's timepiece showed an error of $1\frac{1}{4}'$ of longitude—well under the limits required to win the great prize. Maskelyne, however, disputed the results, and the Board refused to give Harrison the complete prize; but it did vote him a part payment of £2,500, and ordered further trials.

In 1763, in the care of Maskelyne, Harrison's No. 4 was shipped on a voyage to Barbados. The voyage was, in fact, a duel to the death between man and the lunar distances, and Harrison's steadily ticking timepiece. The timepiece won with a calculated error of $1'$ of arc to $4'$ error for Maskelyne and his star tables. The balance of the prize money was not paid until Harrison rallied friends to his assistance, and sent a petition to Parliament, pointing out the injustice that had been done. At the age of eighty, after forty years of work, Harrison received the balance of the money due him. He died in 1776 at the age of eighty-three.

The timepiece of John Harrison showed that longitude could be determined with great accuracy by its use, but he did not invent the chronometer. Others who were working on the problem at the same time, and who followed him, developed the marine chronometer as it is known today. The principle of the detent escapement was invented by Pierre Leroy of France in 1769, and a timepiece made by him made a record in tests at sea equal to that made by Harrison's timepiece. The detent escapement used in present chronometers was perfected by Ferdinand Berthoud, a Swiss, about 1775. The name chronometer was given to the marine timepiece by John Arnold, an English watchmaker, who conceived the helical balance spring as used today, and made further improvements in the detent escapement. The final touch was given to the chronometer through the refinements of another English watchmaker, Thomas Earnshaw, around 1781. It has remained in virtually the same form until recent days.

The English Board of Longitude made its first award in 1737; its last in 1815. The awards totaled £101,000, or at normal par value, over $500,000. In France and Switzerland, the government also paid out substantial sums for exceptionally fine chronometers. It is probable that the total prize money from all countries, which in later years included the United States, would exceed $1,000,000. The value of chronometers in navigation amply justifies the great cost.

The ship's chronometer differs from a watch largely in its balance and escapement. In the ordinary watch, the escapement locks and unlocks five times per second. To produce this rapid action, the balance has a flat, coiled spring. The chronometer escapement locks and unlocks twice per second. The movement of the balance is thus much slower than in the watch. The required increased power was provided by two helical balance springs, one over and one under the balance wheel. Modern chronometers have a single balance spring. The escapement is also of special design.

Chronometers are usually cased in brass, and measure from two to five inches in diameter. The thickness is commonly slightly more than half the diameter. The chronometer is pivoted in a ring, which in turn is held to a box by pivots at right angles to those which support the chronometer. It is poised so delicately that, except during extremely violent motions of the ship, its dial always remains level. Its major fault is that it sometimes stops when given a violent shock during severe storms.

The general use of chronometers on ships did not free the navigators from problems. A careful log of temperature and barometric pressure had to be maintained in order that the errors of the chronometers, due to these factors, could be taken into account. In later years, large ships carried three chronometers, and in violation of the laws of probability, followed the majority if two showed one time, and a third another.

To determine longitude, after 1884, all ship's chronometers were set to the time of Greenwich at longitude 0°. Every 15° of longitude corresponds to an hour of time. Local time was determined when the sun reached its zenith, as shown by the sextant. At that instant, the navigator walked deliberately from the bridge to the chart room where the chronometer was kept, carefully counting seconds as he walked. Still counting seconds, he bent over the chronometer and tried to deduct mentally the seconds elapsed since his observation, from the time shown on the chronometer. Obviously, a considerable error could always be expected.

This gave birth to the deck watch, a large watch which could be set with the chronometer and carried onto the bridge. By glancing quickly from sextant to watch, the local noontime could be established with much greater accuracy.

In modern navigation, with the universal accessibility of accurate radio time signals, calculation for chronometer error has been eliminated, and an ordinary wrist watch could do the job quite accurately.

The trend now is toward synchronous electronic time systems for modern ships, but they still carry fine chronometers, mounted in handsome brass-bound mahogany boxes, and hung on gimbals, to keep the dials always horizontal. They are as much a part of the tradition of the sea as the gold braid on an admiral's cap.

In this Chapter, we have had to compress the events of five hundred years into a few pages, and much of importance has necessarily been omitted. The actual progress of the chronometer, in the century required for its perfection, required the attention of many more hands and minds than those mentioned. In the manufacture of chronometers, England led the world for many decades, and there are still fine chronometers made there. Several firms in the United States also make chronometers of excellent quality. Both the English and American chronometers have shown amazing durability and many, made more than fifty years ago, are still being used. The most accurate marine chronometers of today are being made in Switzerland.

Marine Chronometers and Ship's Clocks

Some people confuse marine chronometers with ship's clocks. The first is used for navigation, the ship's clocks for ordering the day's business on the ship. When at sea, day begins at noon and the tours of duty of the ship's company are divided into watches. On shipboard, most ship's clocks do not strike; the bell is sounded by hand on the bridge every half-hour, a custom which originated in the days of Columbus to mark the turning of the half-hour sandglass. On the half-hour, one bell is struck; on the hour, two bells in quick succession, followed by a pause. Eight bells is struck: dingding / dingding / dingding / dingding. The tidy, round, brass-cased clocks purchased for yachts and home use have a clear, high-pitched bell which strikes in shipboard fashion.

The rotation of the tours of duty for the ship's company at sea begins with the sounding of eight bells at noon. Then follows:

First Watch	12:00 N.	to	4:00 P.M.
First Dogwatch	4:00 P.M.	to	6:00 P.M.
Second Dogwatch	6:00 P.M.	to	8:00 P.M.
Middle Watch	8:00 P.M.	to	12:00 M.
Night Watch	12:00 M.	to	4:00 A.M.
Morning Watch	4:00 A.M.	to	8:00 A.M.
Forenoon Watch	8:00 A.M.	to	12:00 N.

The two two-hour dogwatches provide automatic rotation of the tours of duty among the crew. Except for the first dogwatch, all watches end: *Eight bells and all is well!*

CHAPTER VII

The Development of the Watch

The Birthyear of the Watch

THE WATCH WAS first a mechanical curiosity, then a toy, bauble, or article of adornment, and finally, at long last, a serious timepiece. This metamorphosis required almost three centuries. In all this period, there was no *manufacture* of watches, as we know the term, nor were watches commonly used. They were, for the most part, made to the order of a king or noble, a prince of the church and, to a lesser extent, to the order of a rich banker. Many watchmakers were attached to royal households—"watchmaker to the king" was a position of considerable importance. As quoted in Paul M. Chamberlain's book *It's About Time:*

> Jacques Thuret, watchmaker to Louis XIV, had lodgings in the galleries of the Louvre reserved for the most skillful artisans of Paris, and received 395 livres [about $90] per quarter. He dined at the Chateau at the table of the valets de chambre, and entered the King's apartments with the first gentlemen of the chambre each morning at the dressing of the King, the horologist on duty setting and winding the watch the King was to use and carrying it to him.

Originally the novelty of the watch, and later its richness and beauty made it a prime gift of royalty, and a tool of diplomacy bestowed in thanks for a favor given or anticipated. This fact accounts for the relatively rapid dissemination of knowledge of watchmaking throughout Europe and England—watches received as gifts were turned over to the court watchmaker to be copied or improved upon.

The invention of the watch was made possible by substituting a spiral spring as a source of power for the weight suspended on cord wound around a drum, which was the manner of giving power to the clock. The invention of the mainspring, as it is now called, has been generally credited to Peter Henlein, a locksmith of Nuremberg, around 1500. "Every day," wrote Johannes Cocclaeus in 1511, "produces more ingenious inventions. A clever and comparatively young

76

man, Peter Henlein, creates works of art that are the admiration of leading mathematicians for, out of a little iron, he constructs clocks with numerous wheels which, without any impulse, in any position, indicate the time and strike, and which can be carried on the bosom or in the purse." Italian authorities have disputed the priority of Henlein to the invention, and none of the creations of Henlein have been preserved.

Drawing out a piece of steel to the form of a long spring on the anvil, by hand hammer, with patient heating and reheating, and then finishing it with a file to even width and thickness to the size required even in a bulky timepiece, is an achievement to which the world owes respect. All mainsprings for years after Henlein had to be made in this fashion.

The date 1500, which is given as the probable birthyear of the watch, is also that which historians give to the beginning of the transition of Europe from medieval to modern times. It was the period of preparation for the Renaissance, which led into the eighteenth and nineteenth centuries, in which man's way of life, if not man himself, underwent a revolution. Printing had been evolved from the idea of movable blocks which Marco Polo had reported having seen in China. Europe had learned to make paper, and freed itself from dependence on the papyrus of Egypt. Soon, the effect of the discovery of the new world shifted the centers of wealth and progress from Venice, Genoa, and Florence to London, Paris, and the northern countries of Europe. The mantle of culture worn in turn by Egypt, Greece, Rome, Arabia, and the Italian city-states, fell on new shoulders. All these events affected the progress of watchmaking.

The date 1500 also marks practically the beginning of the conflicts between the two theological beliefs: salvation through the sacraments, and salvation through faith, which divided Christians into Catholic and Protestant camps, and kept Europe in war for a full century. This, too, had a profound effect on the story of the watch. It made Geneva the seat of the greatest watchmaking center.

Portable table clocks, out of which watches evolved, were largely made to a uniform pattern. They were drum-shaped. The dials were horizontal. There was a single hand, the hour hand. All of them rang bells, either on the hour or by an alarm arrangement. The round, straight-sided cases, first made of iron and then of brass, were pierced to let the sound of the bell come through. The movements were held between solid plates separated by pillars which were fastened with pegs. Screws were first used around 1560. The evolution of the portable watch from the table clock required simply a slight reduction in the size of the movement, and a change in the case from drum-shape to ball-shape and egg-shape. Basically, the movements were identical, and the bells were retained. The watches were wound with a key, and probably required frequent winding. They were poor timekeepers. A good watch had an error of an hour or two a day. Some had sundials so they could be set to time at noon.

Watches of this type were made in England, France, Germany, Holland, and Switzerland during the sixteenth century. The mainspring was not housed in a barrel, as now. It resembled, in form, the mainspring of the common alarm clock of today. The first barrel housings for the mainspring appeared around 1575. These early watches suffered a great loss of accuracy because the strength of the mainspring became weaker as it unwound, numerous devices were employed to overcome this difficulty, among which are the fusee and the stack-freed. A hog's bristle to control the motion of the balance was the forerunner of the balance spring. These became obsolete as more solid systems were evolved.

Calvin and Geneva

Much of the refinement of watches occurred in the city of Geneva which, in this period, was subject to the Duke of Savoy. As early as 1419, monumental clocks had been made in this city, one being placed in the Saint Pierre, the cathedral of Geneva. Table clocks in the German manner, were made from around 1500. The fame of the city, however, came from its *orfèvres,* or goldsmiths. The craft included lapidaries, the cutters of precious stones; engravers; goldbeaters, for the making of gold leaf; and other artisans. Goldsmiths also struck the coinage, and some were bankers. Only at Blois, then the seat of the French kings, was jewelry of equal luxury and magnificence produced. At the height of its glory, so to speak, the jewelry trade was given what seemed to be a death sentence. It happened this way.

One of the leaders of the Reformation was John Calvin, who was born in Geneva in 1509. Sent to France, he was first educated for the priesthood, and then switched to law. By day he studied law, by night he continued his studies of the Bible and theology. In time, he embraced the tenets of the reformers. Like others, his history was a succession of success and persecution, of welcome and then flight to one city after another. He returned to Geneva in 1536, and led the movement that freed the city from the domination of the Duke of Savoy. In Geneva, libertinism in faith and morals was the order of the day, and Calvin made attempts to prohibit worldly amusements, which were strongly resisted. In 1538, the Libertines gained control of the government; the church was muzzled, and Calvin banished. In 1541, the conservative element again came into power, and Calvin was asked to return. Calvin demanded, and was given authority to enforce conformance with the disciplines which he considered essential for a Christian community. The consistory of the church, as he organized it, became the tribunal of all morals. One of its acts was to prohibit the manufacture or wearing of jewelry.

The *orfèvres,* who had dabbled in watchmaking, now turned their entire efforts to their fabrication. They added little to the design and mechanical principles of watchmaking as it was being practiced elsewhere. But, from their training in beautiful workmanship, they were able to add a delicacy of execution that resulted in better watches. They were able to reduce the size of the movements. Many enormously complicated timepieces which gave astronomical information were also fashioned. Many French Huguenots who had worked as watchmakers at Blois, and fled from persecution in Catholic France, were welcomed to Geneva. In 1564, John Calvin died, and shortly the restrictions which he had imposed, and which had made Geneva the most moral city in Europe, began to be relaxed under public pressure, aided by patrician families. The *orfèvres* did not abandon watchmaking, but made watches the foundation on which the most elegant articles of jewelry could be superimposed. The age of ornamentation in watchmaking began.

Calvin had prohibited the making or wearing of Latin crosses. A favorite design for ladies' watches, under the new liberalism, was fashioned in just this form—tiny crosses, with the dial ornamented by religious themes in delicate miniature painting, the cross outlined with pearls or diamonds. They were called Abesses' watches, and were hung from a chain around the neck. Others, of more macabre symbolism, were placed in miniature grinning skulls. Cases were fashioned in the form of animals—dogs, rabbits, foxes, and others—generally hammered out of silver. Watch cases were engraved, painted, carved, bejeweled; even the movements were decorated over-all with engraving or special finishes. The pillars which separated the top and bottom plates of the watch movements were "styled" in Egyptian, Roman, tulip, or other forms; the styling so dated that among collectors, the form of the pillars often reveals the place and time of origin.

Watchmaking Becomes a Craft

Workers in this period were closely organized into guilds, which regulated the term of apprenticeship, and the number of apprentices allowed to each master. Young men were bound over to a master, and for a period of years, worked for board and lodging until graduation to journeyman. Craftsmen of reputation could even command fees from apprentices. Though free, the journeyman had to work another period of years at small wages before being admitted to the rank of master. Even then, he had to submit as his "thesis" an exceptional piece of watchmaking as proof of his skill.

The first watch- and clockmakers, as has been told, were the armorers, blacksmiths, locksmiths, and goldsmiths. A clockmaker's guild was formed in Paris in 1544. The first watchmaker's guild received its corporate charter from the city of Geneva in 1601. It thus required a century and a year from the making of the first watch to the recognition of watchmaking as a separate craft. The English watch guild "The Masters, Wardens and Fellowship of the Art and Mystery of Clockmaking of the City of London," chartered by Charles I in 1631, was also given control of the making and selling of clocks and watches in the city of London and for the area ten miles surrounding it. This monopoly, at first a virtue, finally doomed London as a major watchmaking center because foreign improvements, of which there were many, were not permitted, and the inevitable smuggling which ensued did the rest.

Queen Elizabeth's Watches

The popularity of watches with royalty is revealed in the inventory of watches owned by Queen Elizabeth, and published after her death in 1603. The good Queen often complained during her life that no two of her watches told the same time, and there was equal variety in the styles of her watches, which included:

> Item. One clocke of golde wrought like deyses and paunseyes [daisies and pansies] garnished with little sparkes of diamonds, rubies, and emerodes, and eight small pearles on the border, and a pendant acorn.
>
> Item. A watche of agatte made like an egg garnished with golde.
>
> Item. A little watche of golde enameled with sundry colors on both sides alike.
>
> Item. A little watche of christall slightly garnished with golde, with her Ma'ties [Majesty's] picture on it. (From Theodore P. Cuss, *The Story of Watches.*)

Watches cased in rock crystal, like that in the collection of Queen Elizabeth, led to the use of a glass or crystal over the dial, which began to be standard after 1610.

The first big fundamental improvement in watches was the application of a straight spring to limit and control the oscillations of the balance. This was the invention of an English mathematician and scientist Dr. Robert Hooke. With greater uniformity in the motion of the balance, there was considerable improvement in accuracy. This idea was improved upon by Thomas Tompion, called the "father of English watchmaking," who applied to it a regulator by which the effective length of the spring, and consequently its stiffness, could be altered simply by moving a lever. An evolution of this basic principle is found in all watches of today, with the lever movable over a small arc marked F at one end to go faster, and S at the other, to go slower.

Christian Huygens' Great Invention

In 1674, came a still greater improvement with the invention of the coiled balance spring by the great Dutch scientist Christian Huygens. This same genius also successfully applied the pendulum to the clock, as will be detailed in the next Chapter. Unlike his presentation of the pendulum, Huygens merely sparked the idea for the coiled balance spring, without working out the principles for its best use. It can be observed here that the study of this seemingly simple thing is still under way.

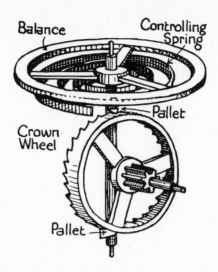

When the balance spring was first applied to watches, the crown wheel was still at right angles to it. This resulted in thick watches. Thin watches became possible when the crown wheel was superseded by an escape wheel parallel to the balance, around 1670.

These inventions led to such great improvement in the running of watches that in 1680 Daniel Quare, another English watchmaker, for the first time made a watch with a minute hand, as well as the single hour hand used up to this time. Within a few years, this too became standard.

The Repeater

Daniel Quare (1648–1725) was an English Quaker, a friend of William Penn, and likewise of King George III. We have noted that early watches generally either had a striking or an alarm mechanism. With the preference for thinner watches (and the term is used in a relative sense), the alarm mechanism was frequently omitted. As a result of the Puritan movement in England, a plain watch, free from any ornamentation and to be worn concealed in the pocket, was introduced, and soon became the standard for English gentlemen. Custom decreed, however, that it was improper to take one's watch from the pocket and consult it when in company. The problem was solved by the repeating watch—a striking watch that was silent until one pressed certain levers or pins. The basic idea for the repeater may have been that of Edward Barlow. It seemed that some people were kept awake by the continuous striking of clocks. Barlow devised a system whereby the clock did not strike unless one pulled a string kept within the canopies of the bed, whereupon the clock chimed out the hour and the nearest quarter. Both Barlow and Daniel Quare later applied the idea to watches. The first repeating watches repeated the hour and quarter, as the clocks had done. Later repeaters were made that would strike the hours, quarters, and minutes. A minute repeater striking 2:33 would sound: ting, ting (the hours); ting-tang, ting-tang (two quarters); tang, tang, tang (three minutes).

Repeaters are marvels of ingenuity, and enormously complicated. Good watchmakers, up to the advent of the wrist watch, continued to make them, and a few are made today. In the Gay Nineties, the repeater was a natural accompaniment for the large diamond stickpin, or something that one could afford if he had a footman for his carriage.

In recent history, after World War II well-intentioned people broadcast appeals for the donation of repeating watches for blinded soldiers, and hundreds were taken out of collections and given to various agencies for this purpose. Few of those who gave, or those who received them, appreciated either their complexities, or their inherent delicacy, nor did they know that out of the forty thousand-odd watch repairers in the United States, those competent to clean and repair a repeater are few indeed, and hard to locate. A conscientious jeweler will not even open and examine a repeater, except for a charge usually of $25, so great is the danger of injury. An ordinary cleaning job commands $100 or more—if one can find someone to attempt the work.

Two events were to speed up the development of watches toward the end of the seventeenth century. One was the gradual perfection of the pendulum clock which, for the first time, gave a standard against which the accuracy of a watch could be measured; the other was the intensive work on timepieces directed at the development of the marine chronometer.

Jewels and the Detached Lever Escapement

The major addition to watches was the use of jewels as bearings. The method of grinding them to suitable shape was originated by Nicholas Facio in 1680. The invention that at long last made an accurate watch a reality was the detached lever escapement which was made by Thomas Mudge in 1750. At this point, good watches, and particularly good watches at a nominal price, were another century in the future, and their development required the work of hundreds of minds and hands.

Thomas Mudge, born in Exeter, England, in 1715, learned watch- and clock-making as an apprentice to George Graham, and was admitted to the select ranks of the Clockmakers Company at the age of twenty-three. He apparently remained with Graham until the latter's death in 1751. Mudge was one of the greatest watchmakers of his day. One of his watches, made for Ferdinand, King of Spain, was mounted in the head of a cane. It struck the hours and quarters automatically, but would also strike the minutes if a button was pressed. His great contribution to watchmaking—the detached lever escapement—was incorporated in a watch he made to the order of Queen Charlotte of England about 1759, when he was clockmaker to King George III. The same escape-

The Birth of the Watch. (upper left) *Nuremberg table clock of the sixteenth century, the first type of portable timepiece to evolve from the invention of the mainspring. It had a single hand. Case is bronze gilt with engraving.* (center left) *A German wall clock in iron case of the sixteenth century.* (lower left) *Ornate treatment of the German-type watch by Swiss craftsmen, this watch signed Denis Bordier (1629–1677) of Geneva.* (upper right) *This handsome example in brass gilt is engraved with scenes of the temptation of Adam. German, seventeenth century.* (lower right) *A German watch dated 1560 in engraved brass case.*

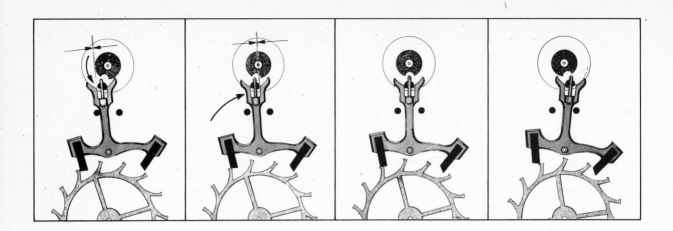

The Action of the Detached Lever or Anchor Escapement. The series of seven diagrams shows in detail how the hands of a watch are turned tick by tock under the control of the balance and the detached lever escapement. In one, *the circular part at the top is a bottom view of the table under the balance. The black semicircular spot is the roller jewel. Below it is the anchor. The two black pieces at the large end of the anchor are the pallet jewels. The straight rod between the fork, or small ends of the anchor, is a guard pin. The two black dots on each side of the shaft of the anchor are banking pins to restrict the maximum movement. If you have seen the inside of a watch, you have noted how the balance wheel oscillates back and forth. In* one, *the balance is moving in the direction of the arrow. The roller jewel has just made contact with the fork. The left pallet jewel rests against a tooth of the escape wheel, preventing it from moving. The escape wheel is under constant tension from the power of the mainspring transmitted through the gears of the watch. In* two, *the left pallet has now raised, which unlocks the escape wheel. The escape wheel moves in a clockwise direction. The whole cycle of operation from* one *to* seven, *is accomplished in 0.01 second or less. At* two, *when the movement of the escape wheel begins, the fork strikes the roller jewel, which gives it the momentum to begin another oscillation. This impulse is assisted by the slant on the bottom of the left pallet jewel. The series of pictures show the sequence until, at* seven, *the escape wheel has again been stopped by the right pallet jewel. At* six, *the roller jewel has cleared the fork, and from here the balance is "detached," or free to continue to rotate until it is brought to a stop by the compression of the balance spring. Then it will rotate in the opposite direction, when the sequence of events will be repeated. In most watches this operation is repeated 5 times per second. In some "fast train" watches, the action is 20 per cent or more faster. In a wrist watch the length of the anchor is about 1/4 inch.*

ment was used in a watch made for Colonel Johns in 1784. It was close to a century before this type of escapement was adopted by watchmakers generally, yet it is basically the same mechanism that is used in the watches of today. The original Queen Charlotte watch is still being used, mounted on an ornate box in the Audience Room of the Queen in Windsor Castle.

The great accuracy revealed by the Queen's watch can be found in a report of its test at King George's private observatory at Kew. Over a period of ten weeks, the accumulated error amounted to four and a half seconds, a record which few watches can equal today. When his friend and patron John Maurice, Count of Brühl and Envoy-Extraordinary from the Kingdom of Saxony to the Court of Great Britain, suggested to Mudge that his invention should be protected by patent, he wrote in reply:

> Your Excellency wishes to have a model of the escapement of her Majesty's watch, that you may be enabled to take proper measure to assert my right to the invention. I am much obliged to you, Sir, for the concern you have always expressed for my interest and honour; and I do not know anything that gives me more pleasure than to contribute, what little I can, to your Excellency's wishes; but there are several objections to what you now ask for. The first and principal is, that I am at present, you know, engaged in a business that will take up a great deal of time, and consequently does not leave me at liberty to prosecute anything else. Another reason, and not a trifling one, is, that although I think, if well executed, it has great merit, and will, in a pocket watch particularly, answer the purpose of time-keeping better than any other at present known; yet you will find very few artists equal to, and fewer still that will give themselves the troubles to arrive at; which takes much from its merit. And as to the honour of the invention, I must confess I am not at all solicitous about it: whoever would rob me of it does me honour. (From Paul M. Chamberlain, *It's About Time*.)

We have mentioned that the detached lever escapement of Mudge was allowed to sleep, so to speak, for almost a century. The escapement that was most generally used during this period was called a cylinder escapement. The basic idea for this escapement is credited to Thomas Tompion. In 1679, an English patent was granted to Tompion, jointly with Edward Barlow and William Houghton, "for a new sort of clock," in which this escapement was used. The cylinder escapement superseded the verge which had been used in some form from earliest days. It was later improved by George Graham, Bréguet, and others, and although now entirely obsolete, was used in watches as late as 1880.

Dr. Guillaume's Contribution

Perhaps the last of the major improvements in watch design resulted from the work of Dr. Charles Edouard Guillaume, while Director of the International Bureau of Weights and Measures at Sèvres, France. The standard meter which

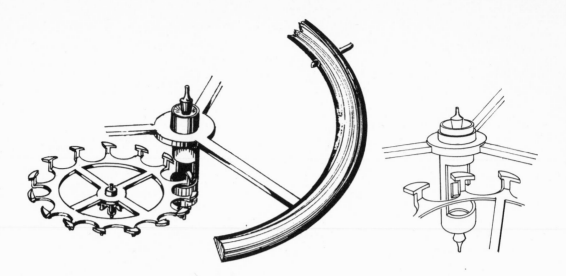

Cylinder escapement which was commonly used in watches from about 1700 until about 1880. The solid balance wheel was supported by three arms. (The spring is not shown.) The cylinder below the balance was cut out to expose a semicircular bearing surface with which one tooth of the escape wheel was always in contact. As the balance rotated first in one direction and then the other, the rotating cylinder released one tooth of the escape wheel at a time. In fine quality escapements, the cylinder was formed from ruby. The great disadvantage of this escapement was the constant friction between the cylinder and escape-wheel tooth which thus interfered with the movement of the balance. The detached lever escapement which replaced the cylinder made possible an enormous improvement in accuracy.

reposed at the Bureau was made of platinum-irridium. Dr. Guillaume set out to discover a less costly metallic alloy which would be resistant to changes in length with temperature. After countless experiments, he found the answer in a nickel-steel alloy, which he named *invar* for invariable, and for which he received the Nobel prize in 1920. Dr. Guillaume suggested the use of invar for balance wheels and pendulums, and later developed another steel-nickel-chrome alloy called *elinvar,* which retains a uniformity of strength under a wide range of temperatures. The watchmaking world was astonished that a problem with which it had struggled to solve mechanically, could be overcome by the use of metals. Other alloys were then sought, and a number of special alloys have been produced. One using berillium, which resists temperature as effectively as invar and elinvar, is also, to a large degree, antimagnetic.

The story of the development of the balance wheel and balance spring up to Dr. Guillaume covers a period of almost two and a half centuries, from 1660 to 1897. Hundreds of watchmakers worked to solve the problem of how to make a watch keep the same time in heat and cold. The best solution found was a cut, bimetallic balance with an overcoil hairspring. The bimetallic balance consisted of two bands of metal, brass on the outside and steel on the in-

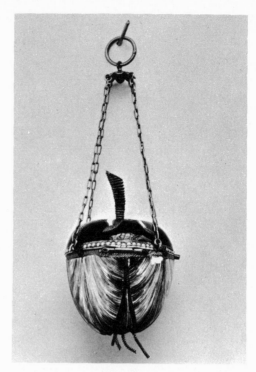

Fantasy Watches. Watches of the seventeenth and early eighteenth centuries. (upper left) Abbesses' watch made by Conrad Kreizer, Strassburg. In gilt, enamel, and rock crystal, the latter forecasting the coming of the watch glass or crystal. (upper right) Acorn-shaped pendant watch in gold and enamel, signed Monée, circa 1770. (lower left) Exquisitely carved watch in the macabre form of a skull. Made by Isaac Penard, one of the famous goldsmiths at Blois, seat of the French royal family, circa 1600. (lower right) Watch in case of rock crystal and gold by Pierre Scheult, Paris, circa 1630.

side, which were attached to the arms of the balance at one end only. Due to the difference in response to temperature changes of the two metals, the free ends moved outward from the original circular form when chilled, and inward when heated. This produced some temperature compensation. Later, a number of movable screws were inserted in the rim of the balance, by which further correction of temperature error could be made. However, the hairspring was also affected. It lost elasticity in heat and gained it in cold, and also changed in length. The famous French watchmaker Bréguet conceived the idea of using an overcoil at the end of the conventional flat spiral spring, which materially improved the timing.

In spite of all efforts, while the difference in rate between heat and cold was to a large degree eliminated, the middle temperature error remained. The great variation in the three temperatures was greatly minimized by the invar and elinvar. More important, the combination of the cut, bimetallic balance and overcoil hairspring were costly to make and difficult to adjust, and were only used in watches of the highest grade. Dr. Guillaume's invention, and others that followed, made possible a substantial improvement in the accuracy of watches of moderate cost.

The now common method of setting a watch by pulling out the crown or stem, and winding it by the same means, did not become common in watches until close to 1870. Watches were wound with a key inserted either through a hole in the dial (as with some clocks today), or through a hole in the back of the inner case. A smaller key, usually on the other end of the larger one, was used to set the hands. Many watchmakers had, from time to time, tried to eliminate the use of keys. Perhaps the first was Beaumarchais, born as Pierre Augustin Caron, who is better known as the author of the plays *The Barber of Seville* and *The Marriage of Figaro,* and perhaps the most influential single individual in inducing Louis XV of France to grant a loan to the youthful American republic to help finance the War of Independence. In his youth, Caron learned watchmaking from his father, who was watchmaker to the King, and from his brother-in-law Jean Antoine Lépine. His keyless watch was an amazingly diminutive creation, mounted in a finger ring which he made for Madame Pompadour about 1752. The watch was wound by rotating the outer rim, or bezel. This idea has been revived briefly from time to time.

Several suggestions for a stem winding system later appeared, including one made by Louis Audemars in Switzerland in 1838. Another version was created by Antoine LeCoultre around 1846. The system most commonly employed, in principle, was invented by Adrien Philippe in 1842. He tried, without success, to interest some watch manufacturer in it. In 1844, at the Paris Exposition, he found a double reward: his invention won a medal, and Count Patek, a Polish nobleman who owned a watch manufacturing business in Geneva, offered him a partnership. The mechanical genius of Philippe had much to do with the early success of the firm of Patek-Philippe.

CHAPTER VIII

The Pendulum

Galileo and the Pendulum

DEAR TO THE LORE of watchmaking is the story of the discovery of the pendulum by Galileo. In 1583, so the story goes, Galileo, when a youth of seventeen, was seated in the baptistery of the cathedral of his native Pisa. There he noted the altar lamp gently swinging to and fro. Impressed by the regularity of the interval of each swing, he timed the intervals with his pulse, and concluded erroneously that regardless of whether the arcs of the swings were short or long, the periods were uniform in time; i.e., isochronous, of equal time. Shortly before his death in 1642, Galileo was in correspondence with the "States General of the United Provinces of the Low Countries" (Holland or the Netherlands as of today) with reference to the problem of finding the longitude. As one of four possible methods, he suggested the development of an accurate timepiece, using a pendulum. By this time, Galileo was totally blind, but he dictated instructions for building the clock to his son Vincenzo for which he designed a unique escapement. Vincenzo made the design for the clock after his father's death, but the clock itself was never completed.

The oscillations of a pendulum are not isochronous, except when the arcs of the swings are identical; a long swing takes more time than a short one. This fact was first noted by the Dutch scientist Christian Huygens, a contemporary and friend of Isaac Newton, and a Fellow of the Royal Society of London. He also assisted in the creation of the Royal Academy of Science of Paris, at the invitation of Louis XIV. He was an astronomer of note, created improvements in the telescope, and discovered the ring of the planet Saturn. His interest in the pendulum, like that of Galileo, was due to the absorbing problem of finding the longitude. Huygens designed, and had made, several types of pendulum clocks, the first in 1657. In 1673, he published *Horologium Oscillatorium,* in which he described his various experimental timepieces, and set forth the mathematical laws affecting the vibrations of a pendulum. As mentioned previously, the pendulum clock which he created as a marine timepiece failed in a test at

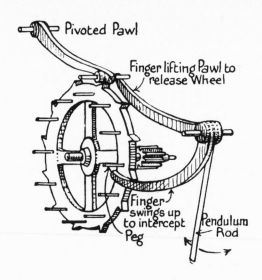

Escapement designed by Galileo.

sea, but the pendulum proved to be one of the most important contributions to the art and science of timekeeping.

The pendulum was most versatile. It could be applied to a spring-driven clock by simple changes, with a tremendous gain in accuracy, reducing an error from an hour or two a day to minutes. Similar results were secured with the weight-driven clock. Since a long pendulum with a short swing produced good time-keeping, the long case, or grandfather clock, was soon evolved, and examples have survived which were made around 1700. The inherent accuracy possible with a pendulum clock initiated an enormous amount of work in the creation of superaccurate timepieces for astronomical purposes.

The principle of the pendulum is simplicity itself. Many of us have rolled a piece of paper into a ball, tied it to a string, and hung it from a table to amuse a kitten. When given a push, it swings back and forth, the swings getting shorter and shorter until it finally hangs straight and motionless. But, if the kitten is interested, and once in a while strikes it with a paw, it will keep on swinging, somewhat erratically perhaps, until he gets tired and looks for other amusement. The paper ball on a string is a simple pendulum. We can liken the kitten to the escapement. Constantly under tension from either spring or weight, the hands move forward as each tooth is released, and by the same motion the pendulum is given a little push, which keeps it swinging.

The problems, of course, are many. The rod of the pendulum, whether of wood or iron, expands with heat and contracts with cold, thereby making the swings longer or shorter. Temperature also affects the bob. The shape of the bob, causing more or less air resistance, is also a factor. The method of suspending the pendulum is also important. The design of the escapement also contributes or detracts from the pendulum action and affects accuracy. The ideal escapement delivers its impulse at the precise moment when the pendulum is at rest at the end of its swing, and always with just sufficient force to cause it to swing the other way, to the same point, time after time, day in and day out, indefinitely.

Some Great Clockmakers

The greatest scientific minds of the day were brought to bear on the manifold problems leading to the possibility of creating a perfect timepiece. Dr. Robert Hooke, mentioned earlier, a mathematician, physicist, and astronomer, as well as a horologist, was one of these. His dictum concerning springs—"As the tension, so is the force"—known as Hooke's Law, is basic to mechanics. He developed an improved escapement for pendulum clocks for astronomical use. Thomas Tompion applied Hooke's escapement to the grandfather clock. Clocks made by Tompion are found in all the great collections, and are highly prized for their meticulous workmanship. George Graham, perhaps more than any of the others, advanced the accuracy of the pendulum clock through his dead-beat escapement which, after two hundred years, is still considered to be the most perfect for its purpose. He also created the mercurial pendulum bob, which greatly freed clocks from errors due to changes in temperature. Julian Leroy, who in France occupied a position in horology comparable to that of Tompion in England, greatly raised the standard of mechanical construction of both clocks and watches, and perfected capillary oiling, a basic achievement to the art. John Harrison, who won the prize for his marine chronometer, created an escapement with which astronomical clocks of excellent accuracy were made; and there were many others in France, Switzerland, and England.

The simplicity with which fair timepieces could be built is illustrated by the clocks made by Eli Terry in Plymouth, Massachusetts, which are so highly prized by collectors. Terry learned the trade of clockmaking by serving a long apprenticeship with Thomas Harland, a skilled watch- and clockmaker who had mastered the trade in England, and set up business in Norwich, Connecticut. Terry made his first clocks in 1786. The works, case, hands, and dial were made of wood, the gears being carved from oak. Crude as they were, the early Terry clocks told time to the entire satisfaction of his customers. In later years, the enterprise started by Terry evolved into the Seth Thomas Clock Company, a name familiar to all.

Astronomical Clocks

Astronomical pendulum clocks gave astronomers their most effective tool for the study of the heavens since the telescope. Refinements in design and workmanship served to reduce the errors due to outside forces and interior friction. Eventually, when every refinement had been made, further improvement in

A Study in Contrasts. (left) *French wall clock of eighteenth century. The springwound movement is by Ferdinand Berthoud; the elaborate gilt bronze sculptured case by Jacques Caffiere.* (right) *American wagon-spring clock of about 1830. From the private collection of Mr. Henry Fried. Europeans closely guarded their method of making coiled springs. Joseph Ives (1782–1862) patented the "wagon spring," which made possible a 30-day clock. The glass dome cover and pendulum have been removed in the photograph above. This model has an iron frame and base. Later models with wood frames "committed suicide" when, due to the tremendous force of the spring, the works above were torn loose. Working examples are therefore rare. Successful clocks with coiled springs did not appear in America until around 1840.*

*Louis XV clock revealing the elegance of the rococo styling of the period. The movement is by
Gosselin, noted clockmaker. The gilt bronze case is signed St. Germaine. The art of clockmaking
in the grand manner is still a French specialty, although the artisans capable of executing the
work are dwindling in number.*

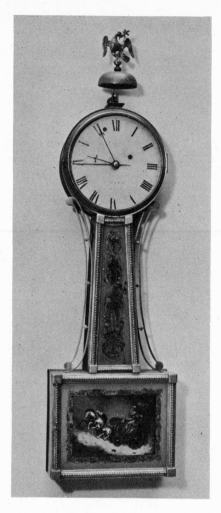

Clocks by Aaron Willard, of the famous Massachusetts family of clockmakers. (right) Grandfather clock. The overdial painting depicts the battle between the Constitution *and the* Guerrière. *(left) Beautiful example of the banjo clock, a style created by Aaron's father Simon, and patented in 1802. It was originally a nonstriking clock.*

*Neuchâtel clocks have been made in the mountainous Jura region of Switzerland since around 1677.
Those illustrated, made in the period from 1750 to 1820, demonstrate the fine decorative crafts-
manship for which Neuchâtel clocks are noted. Many had music boxes, as in one example above.
The styles varied with the ascendency of the various royal houses of Europe for whom most were
made.*

accuracy was effected by placing the entire clock in an airtight case. Today, astronomical clocks work in precisely controlled sealed chambers, where temperatures and atmospheric pressure are virtually constant. The clocks are immovably fastened to brick or concrete pillars which are carried down to bedrock, and are further isolated to insulate the clock from all vibration except from the earth itself. Minor earth shocks, even at a distance of hundreds of miles, disturb such clocks, but these are infrequent occurrences.

Care of Pendulum Clocks

The subject of clocks, and their fascination as objects for collectors, has been admirably covered by many books (see Bibliography) which we will not attempt to duplicate; but, before closing this brief account, we pass along one piece of information which is sometimes omitted from books on clocks which are largely devoted to their picturesque history. Most important to the correct timekeeping of any pendulum clock is the immobility of its running position. A hanging clock should be securely fastened to the wall. A grandfather clock should not only stand on a solid floor, but should further be fastened to the wall by a bracket toward the top of the clock. Mantel clocks present a particular problem because of the temptation to move them when dusting. This problem can be solved by self-discipline. Sensing this problem, makers of some old French clocks mounted them on bases weighing as much as fifty pounds, which made moving them next to impossible. Many people also forget that a clock needs to be cleaned and oiled to keep good time. If the case is dust-tight, cleaning and oiling might be at periods of say, five years. Allowing a clock to run after the oil has been exhausted or fouled with dust, often damages it and makes a repair job necessary. People who purchase old clocks which have been so treated, often find the cost of repair far greater than the price paid for the clock.

The adjustment of a pendulum clock is relatively simple. The clock must be level, so that the swing of the pendulum is equal on both sides of the perpendicular. The pendulum rod must also be perpendicular when viewed from the side, and not lean either forward or backward. When level, the running of the clock should be checked with the same radio time signal at the same hour, for several days, to determine the amount of gain or loss. If the clock is gaining, the screw holding the bob of the pendulum should be unwound to lower the bob on the rod, thus making the pendulum longer. If the clock is losing, the screw should be turned to raise the bob, and thus shorten the pendulum. The screw should be turned a deliberate number of times, say two full turns. Then watch the clock for another few days to see what has happened, and make further adjustments if necessary. The accuracy of the clock will depend on a number of factors, such as quality of construction, age, cleanliness, solidity of its position, etc. When subject to constant vibrations, such as from traffic on a heavily traveled street, no pendulum clock will do its best.

Certain other factors about the pendulum may be of interest. The rebound of the pendulum, when pushed from a perpendicular position, is due to the force of gravity. Galileo, in his experiment of dropping a light ball and a heavy one from the Leaning Tower of Pisa, found that both reached the ground at the same time, and that weight was not a factor. Accordingly, the weight of a pendulum bob has nothing to do with its period of oscillation. The force of gravity is not uniform over the surface of the earth, and when a pendulum clock is moved from one city to another, it may keep time at a different rate. This fact was discovered in 1672, when the French astronomer Richer carried an astronomical clock, adjusted to beat seconds, from Paris to Cayenne. The clock which ran perfectly in Paris lost two and a half minutes a day when set up on this West Indian island. The time of the swing of a simple pendulum is:

$$\text{T (time)} = \pi \frac{l \text{ (length of pendulum)}}{g \text{ (force of gravity)}}$$

Since it was known that l had not changed, the change in T must have been due to a variation in g. Since it is impractical to precisely measure the effect of gravity, any difference is compensated for by adjusting the length of the pendulum. The time of swing of a pendulum is directly the result of its length. The effect of varying the length of a simple pendulum computed for the latitude of New York is shown in this table:

TIME OF SWING	LENGTH OF PENDULUM
½ second	9.78 inches
1 second	39.10 inches
1¼ second	61.15 inches
1½ second	88.10 inches
2 seconds	156.50 inches

The pendulum is, to a considerable degree, affected by barometric pressure. The daily variations due to barometric pressure of a household pendulum clock, in a fixed location, would hardly be perceptible. However, a pendulum adjusted in New York City, at sea level, would require readjustment in Denver, where the altitude is five thousand feet.

The 400-Day Clock

A half century ago, a new kind of clock became popular both in Europe and here. Usually housed in a bell glass to reveal the works, it had a weight suspended from a thin ribbon-shaped, vertical wire which oscillated slowly. It was claimed that these clocks would run 400 days, or more than a full year, on each winding. The weight, originally a solid wheel, in more recent models had a series of brass balls on short spokes, like an old-time gas chandelier. This is a torsion pendulum. Usually it requires 7.5 seconds to rotate in one direction, or 15 seconds for the complete cycle, or 4 times a minute. The thin wire ribbon, under constant tension, becomes a spring when wound up. The suspending wire and its weight function much as the balance wheel and spring of a watch.

The secret of the long running of the 400-day clock can be found in the slow speed of oscillation of its weight, or balance. The balance of a watch, for instance, usually vibrates 300 times per minute, against 4 times a minute for the 400-day clock. This slow motion follows through the clock. Its mainspring barrel makes one turn in 80 days; that of a watch, 6 to 8 turns a day. Such clocks are relatively inexpensive to make, and sell at low prices—so, as in many cases, if their timekeeping is not too good, they make attractive ornaments.

The Atmos Clock

Bearing some small resemblance to the 400-day clock because of the torsion pendulum, the Atmos "perpetual motion clock" is a beautifully conceived and brilliantly executed timepiece. Its pendulum is a temperature-compensated brass wheel. The torsion wire is made of elinvar, an alloy which is relatively unaffected by temperature variations. The pendulum makes a complete cycle of oscillation in one minute. The shafts of all gears turn in jeweled bearings. The combination of slow motion with jeweling, and fine precision construction, reduces both the work load and wear, and largely makes possible the unique Atmos power plant—a compound aneroid barometer by which the clock is kept wound by temperature variations. A change of two degrees is said to be sufficient to provide the power to run the clock for 48 hours. Atmos is capable of extremely accurate timekeeping. Some have run for a year with an accumulated error of a minute or less. But like all pendulum clocks, its accuracy depends on environment—a level base free from vibration representing the ideal.

No mechanical thing exceeds the pendulum clock in longevity. Well-made clocks have run continuously for a hundred years, and still appear to be good for another century or two. There are some people who cannot sleep with a solid pendulum clock ticktocking in the house; but, fortunately, these people are exceptions. To most, the ticktock is a friendly sound, usually not consciously heard, but when heard, merely a sign that life goes on and everything is the best possible "in this best of all possible worlds."

CHAPTER IX

The Watch Factory

Early Watchmaking Machines

THE FIRST WATCHES were made in their entirety by a single craftsman—movement, case, dial, and hand. His tools were a forge, hammer, graver, file, boring tool, and not much else. He drew the gears on metal, and filed them to shape by hand. A single watch represented a year of work. From this simple beginning to the watch factory was a painfully slow journey covering almost three hundred years. For a long period, the number of persons engaged in watchmaking remained small. In 1686, Geneva counted 100 master horologists and 300 apprentices. By 1790, the number had grown to 4,000 and, in that year, around 60,000 watches were produced. These, for the most part, eventually reached the hands of 60,000 members of noble families in almost every country around the world.

Machines for turning blanks and cutting gears were first employed around 1750, but most of the work was still done by hand. A division of the work had now begun, however, and some men were trained as specialists in making certain parts. Casemaking became a separate craft, as did the making of dials, hands, springs, pinions, escapements, and gears. It is recorded that in one shop the making of gears passed through the hands of six different men, from the turning of the blank to final polishing.

In Switzerland, led by the example set by Daniel Jean Richard, a blacksmith who turned watchmaker, the making of some watch parts was given to farm families of the mountain country, where outside activities were brought to a halt when the snow came. By 1781, workers in some 2,000 farm and village homes were filling in their time and adding to their incomes in this way.

The industry thus broke down into parts makers and assemblers. A skilled watchmaker would make a watch, then take it apart and distribute the parts to country and town workers to have them duplicated. When the parts were returned, they were hand-fitted, and the watch was assembled and made to run. This assembling and hand-fitting occupied a skilled mechanic for about

99

fifteen days. By contrast, with the machine-made, interchangeable parts in the factory of today, the same work takes a half-hour or less.

The finest watches were made almost in their entirety in a single shop. A few of these shops managed to make the transition from *cabinotier* to watch factory, but most did not. Those which did survive are among the firms today which enjoy enviable reputations for the quality of their watches. Unfortunately, many celebrated names of olden days are perpetuated in name only, having been adopted decades after the men themselves had gone to their Maker. Among those which have an unbroken record since their beginning are: Vacheron & Constantin, founded in 1783, the patriarch among watchmakers; Agassiz & Company, founded in 1832, which became Longines in 1866; LeCoultre, founded at Le Sentier in 1833; and Patek-Philippe, founded in 1839. Greatest of watchmakers in the prefactory days was Abraham Louis Bréguet. Born in Switzerland, he served his watch apprenticeship in Versailles, and began to make watches under his own name in Paris in 1775. The number of contributions which Bréguet made to watchmaking are legion. His workmanship has never been surpassed, and rarely equalled. An ordinary watch was finished with the precision usually reserved for the micrometer caliper of an observatory. A Bréguet watch commands, even today, the admiration one could only bestow to a true masterpiece.

Voltaire's Experiment

An interesting experiment in the creation of a watch enterprise was undertaken by Voltaire, celebrated French satirist and author. Voltaire had become a rich man through his writings and numerous fortunate speculations, and in 1755, he apparently decided to do justice to his fortune. He purchased an estate at Ferney, a small village near the Swiss border, not far from Geneva, and on it he built small houses to which he invited poets and other literary figures as guests. To this ménage he added watchmaking, creating what he called *Manufacture Royale des Montres de Ferney*. No expense was spared to get the best watchmakers from Geneva, and some excellent watches were produced. Through the capital contributions of its founder, the *Manufacture Royale* had a few years of apparent prosperity. Its demise is attributed to the fact that while Voltaire provided handsomely for making watches, he appropriated nothing for the selling of them—a mistake made later by many others.

In this period, watches were approaching the elegance of today through a sensational innovation of Jean Antoine Lépine, watchmaker to the King of France, who in 1744 conceived the idea of replacing the solid backplate of the watch with separate bridges. This made possible a rearrangement of the parts, which reduced the movement from two layers of parts to one, and thus cut the thickness of the movement in half. Bréguet, in 1810, refined and improved on the Lépine idea and others also worked on it so that by 1846 watch movements were made that were so thin they could be concealed in a gold coin.

By 1790, the scientific study of gear forms and other watch components began, and mathematical formulas were evolved. In 1823, a school of watchmaking was established in Geneva, and this later replaced the apprenticeship system. By 1842, the division of work pointed to the need for specialized training, and separate schools were established.

Let us look at what life was like at this time. Although George Stephenson had constructed a locomotive that went six miles per hour in 1814, by 1842 steam railroad companies rarely spanned more than thirty to forty miles, and horses were the main means of transportation. The wagon trains pictured in movies of the Old Oregon Trail had their counterparts in Europe. The first penny post was established in England in that year. An important invention was that of the woven wick, which a few years later led to the kerosene lamp! The beginning of the Industrial Revolution around 1770 witnessed the breaking up of the duchies and baronies, and distribution of the land among the people. The serfs disappeared, and the small farmer and landowner appeared. This was the beginning of the creation of purchasing power, and a broader market. In 1804, Napoleon became Emperor of France and ruler of most of Europe. By 1815, Napoleon was at St. Helena, and the Congress of Vienna was reorganizing Europe. But the old regime—good things for the privileged few —which lost its first round in the French Revolution in 1792, was as good as dead. Victoria had been Queen of England for three years. Masses of manhood all over the world were awakening as from sleep and stretching their giant muscles. The spirit of change was everywhere.

A big problem of the watch industry in these times was the lack of uniformity of the parts. Every part in every watch had to be retouched and patiently hand-fitted. Machines had cut down the work of basic fabrication, but their work was still too crude to produce parts alike enough to be interchangeable. This was the key to mass production.

The First Mass Production

Actually, the basic problem had been solved by Eli Whitney, noted American inventor. He is best known for his invention of the cotton gin which he undertook as a favor to Mrs. Greene, widow of the famous general of the Revolution, with whom he was boarding while studying law in Savannah. This invention brought him little money, and many costly lawsuits. But in 1789, he secured a contract from the government to make firearms, and made a fortune from the method of manufacture he developed. In his factory at Whitneyville, Connecticut, he produced rifle parts so exactly alike that a hundred rifles could be taken apart, the parts scrambled, and when reassembled, all would work perfectly.

It must be pointed out that up to this time, while clocks were being made, there was no watchmaking in America. Here and there an individual watch might have been made by a single craftsman, but all watches were imported largely from Switzerland or England. Until the Revolution, only English-made watches could be imported legally. In Switzerland, however, there was a highly organized and proficient industry employing at this period around 20,000 workers, which had been slowly building up over a two-hundred-and-fifty-year period.

The American Pioneers

In 1850, two men—Aaron L. Dennison and Edward Howard, both of whom had experience in clockmaking—made a study of the machines used by Whitney to make rifles, and began the construction of a factory to make watches by the same method at Roxbury, Massachusetts, a town not far from Boston. The first three years were occupied with the construction of the machinery. Their first watch was an 8-day pocket watch which was not successful. They then made conventional pocket watches. In 1854, the factory was moved to Waltham, Massachusetts, but soon ran into difficulties and failed in 1857. The assets were purchased by Tracy Baker & Company, casemakers of Philadelphia, and Dennison was retained as superintendent. We will pick up this history later.

Unknown to these courageous pioneers, successful watches with interchangeable parts were already being made in Switzerland. The success was achieved by a mechanical genius, Georges Leschot, who was taken into the Vacheron & Constantin watch factory in 1839. Leschot previously, in 1825, had given the final touch of perfection to the anchor escapement which Mudge had invented a half century earlier. With Vacheron & Constantin he concentrated on two basic tools, a precision pantograph and a micrometer caliper. With the first, he was able to draw gears and other parts in large size with curves exactly calculated, and then reduce these conceptions to the size to be executed. With his caliper he was able to measure parts for exactness and be sure that they met the desired specifications. By 1845, Vacheron & Constantin were producing interchangeable watch parts by machine—but in secret. Patek-Philippe attained the same goal somewhat later.

In 1866, the Longines factory (named after the valley in which the plant was located) began to make a single caliber of key-wound pocket watch with workers from the Agassiz shop. It was a struggling enterprise with less than 25 workers for the first dozen years, but it was making parts by machine.

LeCoultre of Le Sentier, Switzerland, had also been making progress toward precision machine work, and at the first world's fair, that of 1851 in London, received a grand prize for a pinion made by machine for the first time, from a single piece of steel.

To return to the United States, the original Howard and Dennison Company had become the American Watch Company, with a capital of $300,000 in 1860. In 1885, the capital was further increased to $4,000,000, which certainly looks like success, and so it was.

Success at Philadelphia World Fair

At the Philadelphia Centennial Exposition of 1876, the American Watch Company not only put on a magnificent show of watches, but set up a complete factory to show how they made watches by machine. If they had been in the machine business, the move would have been understandable, but what strange course of reasoning induced them to show their competitors elsewhere how they operated, is hard to understand. It must be remembered that while Vacheron & Constantin, Patek-Philippe, Longines, and LeCoultre were making watches by machine, these were watches of the highest grade. The great bulk of watch manufacturing in both Switzerland and England employed machines only to a limited extent. The Swiss delegation, in particular, saw at once why American watches were beginning to crowd them out of some of their world markets for lower-priced watches. The American watches were cheaper, and of quality well above the average. Some of the American watches shown at Philadelphia, which had been carefully finished and well adjusted, performed on a par with the best watches made anywhere.

At the Paris Exposition of 1878, the American Watch Company also exhibited, but did not show machinery. The impression made by the American exhibits can be measured by the drop in importation of Swiss watches to the United States from 330,000 units in 1870 to 134,000 in 1875. Part of this drop can be accounted for by bad business years which climaxed with the panic of 1873.

When M. Favre-Perret, a Swiss judge at the Philadelphia Exposition, returned to Switzerland, he publicly declared that unless something radical was done, the machine-made watches of the United States would ruin the Swiss watch industry. When the Swiss heard that some American companies employed as many as 1,000 men, they were staggered. The nature of the Swiss problem was further shown by comparison of the annual production of watches per man: 40 in Switzerland against 150 in the United States.

The biggest advantage of the machines was the elimination of the need for skilled craftsmen. Boys and girls with brief training could become machine tenders. The precision machines, overnight, so to speak, wiped out the Swiss asset of a corps of the finest mechanics developed through generations of application. In the American factory, out of 1,000 workers only a few—the die and tool makers—were precision workers. This, of course, is the secret of success of all mass production, as later proved in the automobile industry.

Mechanization became a national issue in Switzerland. An enormous program of research was undertaken, in which all members of the industry participated. Today, Swiss watchmaking machinery is the finest made anywhere in the world.

The prosperity of the American Watch Company did not go unnoticed in the United States. Watch companies were organized by the score, and by the score collapsed. When all of the capital invested in watch manufacturing in the United States is balanced against the losses, it must be concluded that one could not look for a less promising venture in which to engage.

Of all the hundreds of watch factories established in the United States, but a few remain. As has been said before, the world's watchmaking industry is small, and watchmaking is not sufficiently profitable to attract venture capital. The Elgin National Watch Company at Elgin, Illinois, was organized by a group of Western capitalists. They had the idea that with $100,000 of capital the job could be done. They made the capital $150,000, and in 1864 began the manufacture of the machinery for making watches. The first watches were ready for market in 1867, but before the company turned the corner and began to be self-supporting, the total capital subscribed by the backers had grown to $500,000. The first factory was vastly different from the watch factory of today. A single machine did a single operation, while today a dozen or more tasks may be performed by the same machine in precise timed sequence. Labor was of the simplest kind—including many boys and girls, as was permitted in those days. The average earnings of the girls was $6 a week, so we learn from a contemporary publication; of the boys, $3 a day. Girls found board and room for $3 a week around town, but males being less desirable to lady boardinghouse keepers, the boys couldn't find quarters for less than $5 a week, and generally it was more.

The first watches were sold as movements only, the casing being done by jewelers, as was common in the industry. Elgin is one of the few pioneer American manufacturers still on the scene, and is today one of the largest in the world.

The Hamilton Watch Factory at Lancaster, Pennsylvania, was organized in 1892, primarily for the manufacture of "railroad" watches. The railroads in this period represented the largest market for accurate pocket watches. It appears that in 1891, there was a head-on collision of two railroad trains near Kipton, Ohio, which investigation showed was caused by a difference of four minutes between the watches of the two engineers of the trains. As a result, strict rules were set up to assure accuracy of railroad watches, which specified a maximum error of thirty seconds a week. Engineers, conductors, brakemen, stationmasters, and others who had to do with running the railroads had to provide themselves with railroad watches. Each watch had to have a certificate of accuracy which had to be renewed every six months. Owners of the watches had to carry a card which traveling inspectors punched with each examination, usually once a month. Watches had to be carried in the vest pocket, and the vest had to be hung up at night so that the position and tem-

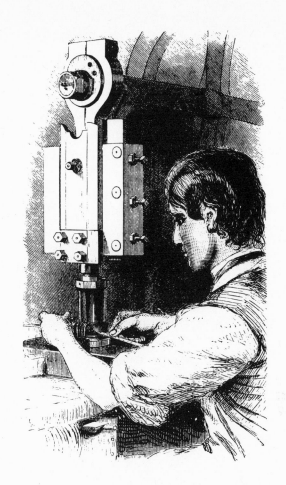

Boys and girls, aided by simple machines, enabled the early American watch factories to match the skill of the craftsmen of Europe, and their background of centuries of experience.

perature of the watch would be disturbed as little as possible. Hamilton succeeded well in this field, although the competition was keen. Today, Hamilton makes watches of all conventional types, and they are close to the finest American quality.

In 1869, there were 37 watch manufacturing companies in the United States. In 1914, there were but 15. Today, the number is less than half.

Switzerland and the U.S.A.

In Switzerland today, watchmaking is an industry in the same sense that automobile manufacture is an industry in the United States. On the other hand, watches are made in the United States by a few more or less self-sufficient factories. The American automobile industry consists of a few "auto makers" who are served by some 20,000 subcontractors or parts makers, who do most of the actual fabrication. In the same way, the great majority of Swiss watch factories are served by some 3,000 separate parts manufacturers, each of whom is a specialist. The finest Swiss watches are, however, still made almost in their entirety within one factory.

The problem of keeping the Swiss factories staffed with competent workers is met with special schools in horology. There are seven such schools with courses varying from two and a half years to five years, depending on the part of the trade to be learned. An engineering course to which students are admitted after graduating from secondary schools turns out men who can eventually serve in the designing rooms and as department heads. A graduate from a school of horology, which is equivalent to a college course, can take postgraduate work at the University of Neuchâtel leading to a degree in horological engineering. Watch factories in the United States establish their own schools, but admittedly cannot compete with the broad program of the Swiss horological schools. The vast difference is further revealed in the literature available for teaching. The Swiss student has several hundred volumes of texts in French and German on watchmaking and its science. Here, we have practically nothing on factory practice except a few English translations of books printed in Switzerland.

The phenomenon of the development of the Swiss watch industry can be called an accident of environment. Switzerland is a small country, with an area of 16,000 square miles—about half the area of Maine; and a population of around 5,000,000—close to that of New Jersey. Important as is the watch industry to this small country, the value of the watch industry *of the world* at factory level is exceeded manifold by more than a hundred American companies in other fields: electronics, office machines, chemicals, automobiles, oils, etc.

Watch factory of 1878. Primly dressed misses work under the watchful eye of a bearded supervisor in the train room of the Elgin Watch Factory.

The Watch That Made the Dollar Famous

At the World Columbian Exposition held at Chicago in 1893, one watch exhibit aroused almost as much astonishment as did the electric lights. Here Robert H. Ingersoll unveiled to the public a watch offered for sale at a price of $1.50. The event was historic for two reasons: first, it introduced the idea of high-powered merchandising to the watch business; and second, it led to the now universal custom of personal watch ownership. With the average worker earning $1 a day or less, and supporting a family of six children, a watch, even at $5, was a luxury that few could afford. The factory whistle signaled work time, lunch time, and quitting time. And then it was dark. The church bells told when it was time to go to service. The little clock on the kitchen mantel or in the parlor was all the time-telling gadget the ordinary man needed.

The brothers Ingersoll started their merchandising career with rubber stamps and a capital of $150. Then followed a toy typewriter at $1, a sewing machine at $1, and other items they sold through jobbers. Then came an excursion into mail-order selling, for which they distributed several million catalogues a year. And finally they experimented with chain stores. In each of these ventures, they were pioneers. Then came the grand idea of a watch to serve the needs of the millions. The price of $1.50 was soon reduced to $1, and the slogan was "The Watch That Made the Dollar Famous." A 5-cent gilt chain was an early selling dodge, and there were many others. Many remember the first watch which was received as a bonus with a suit of clothes. Advertising and merchandising was on a grand scale. In the first twenty-five years, the Ingersolls sold more than 50,000,000 watches, a number considerably larger than all the watches made and sold by others since Henlein created the watch back in 1500.

The First Wrist Watch

Equally significant in the watch business was the advent of the wrist watch. It is believed that the idea of incorporating a watch in a bracelet was first thought of by Nitot, a Parisian jeweler. The first piece was executed at the command of Empress Josephine, wife of Napoleon, as a wedding gift to her son's bride, Princess Auguste-Amélie of Leuchtenberg, in 1809. He made two identical bracelets of gold, pearls, and other stones—in one was a watch, in the other a calendar. Apparently the idea did not appeal to other watchmakers or jewelers. In 1880, the German admiralty approached several Swiss watchmakers to have made what would be considered today conventional men's wrist watches. They were for the use of naval officers. Believing the idea worth exploiting, the factories made others and tried to sell them. A shipment to the United States in 1904 was returned with scorn, and a similar lack of interest was met elsewhere. But in 1910, the idea finally caught on in England, and a wrist watch became *de rigueur* for the well-dressed man. The wearing of a wrist watch was in a class with wearing a handkerchief tucked in the sleeve, another English custom of the period.

Then came 1914, and the outbreak of the First World War. The convenience of the wrist watch for artillery officers and aviators was immediately sensed. Orders went to the factories for wrist watches by the thousand. When America entered the war, she too sensed the need for wrist watches, and placed orders. They were issued eventually to most of the soldiers, and when they returned home, the wrist watch was immediately an accepted accessory.

The sudden interest in wrist watches caught most of the factories of the United States unprepared. To make watches in the new small size required the creation of entirely new watch movements, which takes time and costs money. Many factories decided that the wrist watch was a fad, and wouldn't last. Others couldn't make the switch in time. The mortality of factories was large.

The final event that had its imprint on watch manufacture was the advent of the credit jeweler in the United States, which began around 1920, and made rapid progress. What Ingersoll had done with the $1 pocket watch was repeated for wrist watches by the credit jeweler, who made it possible for millions to buy them for $1 or less down, and 25 cents a week. The new crop of credit jewelers didn't know anything about watches, and initially didn't much care. A watch was something to sell, and in no time became a packaged item like a pack of cigarettes, or a can of peas.

Before the advent of the credit jeweler, fine watches had been sold by a few hundred old-line jewelers who knew watches, and had the greatest respect for them. Watch manufacturers, for the most part, sold movements to these jewelers. The jeweler bought or made the cases. Many watches were eventually sold to the consumer with the name of the jeweler on the dial. Most of the new crop of jewelers didn't want to be bothered with casing, but some did. The manufacturers were forced to refuse to sell any but cased watches, much to the chagrin of the old-timers. Selling this new type of jeweler required a brand new series of techniques. Watches had to be cased, and attractively boxed. Aggressive merchandising and advertising were a sheer necessity. Profit margins of the jewelers had to be increased to cover the cost of carrying accounts. Since the buyers represented a new and previously untouched market, reputation counted for little. Newcomers with no habits to change got into watch merchandising, buying watches from Switzerland and putting their own names on the dials. Bulova and Benrus are two names which went from nothing to a position among the leaders in a few years. Bulova imported a Swiss watch factory almost *in toto,* and is now making a large number of watches in this country.

The First Wrist Watch. These exquisitely fashioned gold bracelets set with pearls and emeralds were made to the order of Empress Josephine, wife of Napoleon, by the Parisian jeweler Nitot in 1809, as a wedding gift for Princess Auguste-Amélie of Leuchtenberg on the occasion of her marriage to Josephine's son Eugène de Beauharnais. The two bracelets were inspired by the custom of ancient Roman emperors. One bracelet carries a watch, the other a calendar.

The watch manufacturing business is still in a state of flux, and no one knows from what direction the next shock will come. Throughout its history, it has had to survive many. There will no doubt be many more, as in all other industries. Change is normal.

Other Watchmaking Countries

In the preceding pages we have spoken principally of Switzerland and the United States, the major watchmaking countries of the past. Some watch- and clockmaking has always been carried on in France, Germany, England, Russia, and Japan. All of these countries are now expanding their manufacturing.

Typical of this expansion is France, which boosted production of complete watches from 2,000,000 in 1938 to 4,700,000 in 1956. These figures, however, do not reveal the full extent of their progress. The 1938 production was achieved largely by the use of movements imported from Switzerland; the 1956 watches were almost wholly French made.

The French watch industry is being methodically developed with government assistance along Swiss lines. There are some 200 manufacturers of rough movements, parts, and components such as dials and hands, and watchmaking tools and machines. These are sold to about 350 concerns who turn out finished watches. Ten companies operate self-contained watch factories where finished watches are made from raw materials.

In addition, there are some 100 clock factories, including a number of small firms which still produce the elaborate works of art for which French clockmakers have long been famous.

The industry co-operatively maintains a research center at Besançon, the site of the famous French observatory. The French government's interest in the watchmaking industry is obviously to increase exports. To that end, it has instituted a quality-control policy, and all exports must carry a certificate issued by the government.

West Germany is rapidly expanding its watch production and is now a significant factor, particularly in the low-price field. Their watches are well-made and cost-cutting features, such as plastic bridges, suggest further innovations to come. The German clock industry, which was important in peacetime, has more than regained the position it once enjoyed. The 400-day clock is a current German specialty.

Japan seems about to repeat, in the watch business, the astounding success which it has achieved in optics, cameras, and radio components. The Hamilton Watch Company is co-operating with Japanese interests to supply tools and technical advice, with the announced intention of producing high-grade watches at low prices, by utilizing cheap Japanese labor.

Soviet Russia acquired a start in the watch industry by acquiring the Deuber-Hampden Watch Factory of Canton, Ohio, and the Ansonia Clock Company of Brooklyn, New York. The Hampden was one of the finest pocket watches produced in the United States, but the factory rapidly lost ground with the introduction of the wrist watch, and at the time it was acquired by the Soviets in the thirties, it had been shut down for some years. Little is known about production from these factories after they were moved to Russia. The recent developments in watchmaking in Soviet Russia have been reported in an article in the *British Jeweller & Metalsworker* by a group of British horologists who visited some of the new Soviet watchmaking establishments. As of 1957, the Soviet industry was producing some 24,000,000 units with a goal of 50,000,000 by 1956. If attained, this would make the U.S.S.R. number one in watch and clockmaking. The industry has the services of a horological research institute with a staff of over 300 technicians. Of the many factories, "Moscow No. 3" specializes in the making of small tools for the industry, "Moscow No. 4" makes mainsprings, and "Moscow No. 5" is devoted exclusively to the making of jewels for watches and instruments. Other factories make complete timepieces except for springs, jewels, cases, and straps.

Watch factories are scattered throughout the country. The workweek is 46 hours. There are 7 statutory holidays during the year, to which is added a 15-day vacation for workers, 24 days for scientists. Some of the factories work 24 hours a day with 3 shifts. The factories are producing marine chronometers, deck watches, pocket watches, timing watches, and ladies' and men's wrist watches. An automatic watch is being planned. The variety of styles in wrist watches is small, the finish not up to Swiss or American standards. A watch costing 36 rubles to make is sold in the state stores for 540 rubles. However, there are no watches other than of Soviet make available for ordinary purchase.

One can conclude that the small but important industry of watchmaking seems headed for rugged competition.

Pocket watch by Ferdinand Berthoud (1727–1807)
with painted enameled back.

CHAPTER X

The Modern Watch

A Product of Evolution

THE MODERN WATCH, as we have seen, has been evolved over centuries of time, with the help of hundreds of watchmakers and scientists. It represents the most outstanding demonstration of the marvels of modern precision manufacturing. A watch of the best quality contains about 130 separate parts, which require something like 1,400 machine operations for their execution. Most of the machines perform several operations. A multiple-drill press, for example, may bore as many as 18 holes in the plate of a watch at one operation with a precision of 0.01 millimeter. Many automatic machines turn out complicated parts of the highest precision with relatively little attention. One man, in some instances, can tend a group of 6 or more machines. The machines include optical positioning tools which can locate a precise point within 0.000001 inch.

Not too many years ago, quality of manufacture was controlled, to a large degree, by the amount of money a manufacturer was willing to spend for tools for cutting, boring, or milling. Precision manufacture demanded that to maintain dimensions and achieve the proper finish, tools had to be changed frequently. The cost of tools accounted for a large part of total manufacturing. The creation of Carboloy by the General Electric Company was as significant as the introduction of machines to manufacturing. Tools tipped with it outlast steel many times. Carboloy and other materials which have been developed have made precision manufacturing both relatively cheap and, to a large degree, have wiped out the great differences in quality which previously existed.

Grades of Watches

Watches, today, are made in several grades. At the top of the triangle are the hand-finished supergrade watches, each of which can be considered perfect. The total production is a few thousand watches a year, and in 18-carat gold cases, their base retail price is around $400 in the United States. We can put them in the Rolls Royce class.

We step down from there to production watches with a base retail price of around $75 to $100. The difference between these and those at the summit is the absence of individual treatment. When given this individual attention, which qualifies them for "chronometer" designation, the price goes up to almost those at the top. To actually adjust a watch to maintain a relatively uniform rate in each of the five positions and three temperatures calls for about a week's work on the part of a highly skilled technician, spread out over a period of perhaps several months. The value of the adjustments can only be demonstrated by meticulous tests in a qualified laboratory.

For most of us, the top grade of production watch with an excellent average quality serves all purposes. Such a watch, given reasonable care, will run within a few seconds a day of accurate time, and should not require resetting more frequently than once a month. The habits of the wearer have a great deal to do with the accuracy realized. All watches run better in one position than in others. Usually, even the best watches run at different rates at several times during twenty-four hours. Over this period, however, gains and losses cancel each other out, and the error is never more than a few seconds.

Below these, we can logically establish two grades: one with a base retail price of about $50, and the other about $30. The difference in price is due to a number of factors: mechanical design; degree of finish of the parts; quality of components, such as jewels, escapement, and balance; overall quality of workmanship; the quality of the case; attachments; boxes; and so forth. The relative value of these two grades, as compared to the top production grade, can be measured by somewhat less accuracy, the probability of less uniformity in quality, and almost definitely, shorter life. The lower of these two grades probably could not be "adjusted," in the correct sense of the word, without an excessive amount of hand work.

All of the above grades would have 17 or more jewels, and anchor escapements with jeweled pallets. Jewels, you should know, have little to do with the performance of a watch. If perfectly made, a watch with 7 jewels could be adjusted to the highest possible degree of accuracy. These would all be associated with the balance and escapement. The most costly watches usually have no more than 17 jewels. No extra number of jewels can change an ordinary watch into a fine watch.

Pin-lever Watches

Next come those with pin-lever escapements, most of which have no jewels at all. Some of these, if made on the Roskopf design, have one less wheel and pinion. Where the fine watch has 130 parts, these may have 70 or less. Some made in Germany have plastic bridges. Manufacturing costs for these movements have been estimated as low as 50 cents.

In the past few years, these watches have been sold in large numbers in

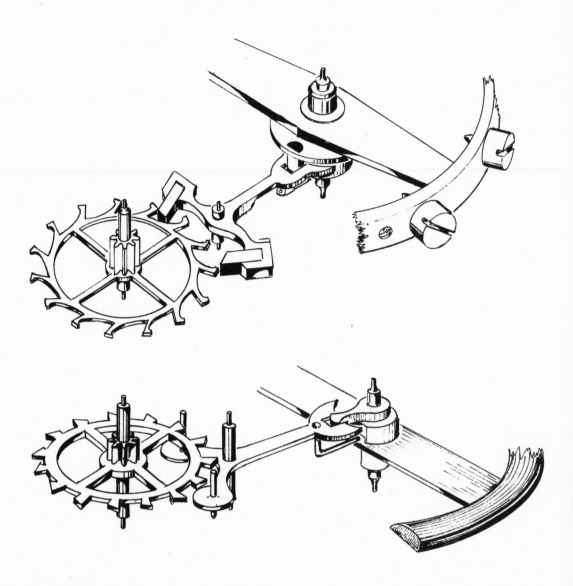

Types of Modern Escapements. (top) *The detached jeweled-lever escapement in the best watches.* (bottom) *The pin-lever escapement used in very low-priced watches. This is the basic invention of Georges Frédéric Roskopf (1813–1889) and part of his "watch for the proletariat" which he produced in 1870. Completely radical in design, even to the elimination of the center wheel and abandonment of any jeweling, Roskopf watches were sold in Switzerland at the then unheard of price of 25 francs. It produced the basic design for the later Ingersoll, and its escapement is perpetuated in the lowest priced watches of today. Casual comparison between the two illustrations reveals the sheer simplicity of design of the pin-lever escapement. And it does permit the "proletariat" to have a watch that tells time "to the hour"!*

cases of anodyzed aluminum in a gold color. Superficially, they look like the real thing. In ladies' watches they have been highly styled and decorated with imitation gems. Because of their styling, they have been used for large-scale promotions, and when advertised as low as $5, have affected the sale of watches of better grade. Eventually, they may be put in the class of costume jewelry, where they belong. Switzerland, France, and Germany are the principal suppliers.

Inexpensive watches are also produced in the United States in great volume. The U. S. Time Corporation, which fell heir to the Ingersoll crown, which it controls along with many other brands, claims to be the largest manufacturer in the world in number of units made. While the imports are distributed largely by jewelers and department stores, which total probably less than 10,000 outlets, the American low-priced watches are distributed on a tremendous scale— perhaps through as many as 200,000 drug, cigar, general, and other stores, from metropolitan cities to tiny villages. The production runs from Mickey Mouse watches for children up to substantial waterproof, shockproof watches for men. Without positive comparative tests, and simply as a matter of reasonable opinion, the American products probably represent better value than their imported counterparts. The imports have enjoyed a temporary advantage in styling, which undoubtedly will be overcome.

Watch Cases

This is a good time to mention something about watch cases. We have mentioned the anodyzed aluminum of the costume-jewelry watch. The aluminum case gives adequate protection to the movement over a short period of time, providing the thickness of the case has not been sacrificed to turn out a very thin watch. Often, however, some distortion takes place which permits the case to leak dust, and eventually the watch will get gummed up and stop. The cost of cleaning would hardly be justified.

Next in order come those made with electroplated gold on brass. These may offer more protection than the aluminum, but the gold plating wears off in a year or so. Not too many of these cases are made.

Then comes rolled gold plate, and probably in the same class, chrome-coated brass. Their life can be estimated at something like five years, conservatively. Better still, is the gold-filled. The difference between rolled gold plate and gold-filled is the amount of gold which is rolled onto the brass core. In gold-filled stock, a minimum of the total weight of the case must be gold of some specified carat, the minimum being 10. (Pure gold is 24-carat.)

Finally, we come to the gold cases which are variously 10, 14, and 18 carat. The higher the carat, the softer the gold, the higher the polish it can take, and the more easily it can be marred by scratches.

Unfortunately, none of these material specifications by themselves are proof

A Half Century of the Lady's Wrist Watch. (upper left) *The previous chatelaine watch gets a golden bracelet.* (lower left) *The large size of the watch is minimized by a filigree and diamond case.* (center) *These two watches feature grosgrain ribbons, a fashion which held for some twenty years.* (upper right) *This is the baguette style where the illusion of smallness is gained by the narrow width.* (inset) *Here is a modern watch of minuscule size where the winding stem has been banished to the back of the watch and thus out of sight.*

of quality. Some gold cases, for example, are far too thin to adequately protect the movements. Some cases do not fit the movements exactly.

The best case, from the standpoint of protection, is stainless steel. For hard service, a waterproof, stainless-steel case assures the greatest dependability in timekeeping.

Watch Features

Shockproof is a term frequently seen in watch advertising. In the shockproof watch, one or both pairs of jewels in which the pivots of the balance staff ride are mounted on some form of spring. On account of the relatively heavy weight of the balance wheel, the balance staff is frequently bent or broken with shock. The springs absorb some of the shock and reduce, but do not entirely eliminate, the chance of damage. If a watch is dropped on some hard surface, damage still occurs. Most of the best manufacturers resisted the use of shock-resistant jewel mounting, but were forced into it by public demand. They held that the absence of rigidity impaired accuracy. Improvements in this device have reduced this danger.

The automatic, or self-winding watch is growing in popularity. The idea is not new. A self-winding pocket watch was made by Abraham-Louis Perrelet around 1770. It had a pendulum mounted on the side of the case, which moved up and down as the wearer walked, and was called a pedometer watch. The same principle is still used in pedometers which, when carried in the pocket, will tell you approximately how far you walk. The basic principle of the modern self-winding wrist watch was invented by an Englishman, John Harwood. Instead of a pendulum mounted on the side of the watch, it provided a rotating weight pivoted at the center of the watch.

The energy of the rotating weight is too slight to wind the mainspring directly, so it is multiplied by a series of gears. There are two types: in one the weight rotates through an arc of about 120° where, at each end, it is arrested by a spring; in the other, the weight is permitted to rotate through 360°. Excellent mechanisms are made using both systems. Some people, however, become conscious of the slight thump which is made when the weight is arrested by the spring in the first type.

Theoretically, the self-winding watch is more accurate than a hand-wound watch, because the mainspring is always fully powered. Actually, this is not always the case. In order to prevent overwinding, the mainspring is not attached to the inside of the barrel. Instead, there is a friction connection by means of a piece of curved, stiff spring on the end of the mainspring. When the watch is fully wound, this clutch arrangement slips along the inside of the barrel. It requires very careful adjustment and lubrication to make this work right. Watch repairers, as a rule, make the adjustment so that the slip takes place before the mainspring is actually fully wound.

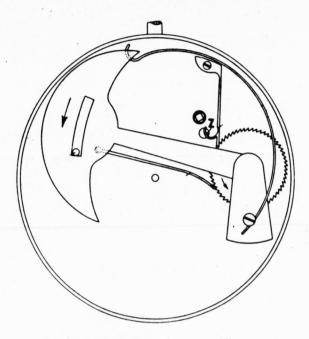

The self-winding pocket watch of the eighteenth century. The pendu-
lum, lightly supported by a spring, moved downward with each step of
the wearer. A similar mechanism is used in the pedometer watch which
tells approximately how far one walks.

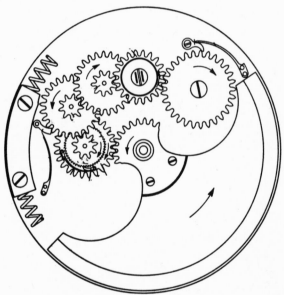

One Form of the Automatic or Self-winding Wrist Watch. As the
weighted segment rotates through an arc of about 120° with the move-
ment of the wrist, the force is multiplied by a series of gears and pinions
producing an almost continuous series of slight winding actions. Buffer
springs stop the rotor at each end of its swing. Another system employs
a weight which can rotate in either direction through 360° with a
slightly more complicated gearing system.

Self-winding introduces many extra parts, and adds the considerable strain of the rotating weight. Self-winding watches cost more to clean and probably will not last as long as comparable hand-wound watches. However, they are probably here to stay.

Antimagnetic is another term one meets in watch advertising. The use of the term is justified by the use of alloys instead of steel in the balance and its spring. They are antimagnetic against the magnetic fields found around the home. They are not antimagnetic when exposed to strong magnetic fields such as are found around commercial electrical systems, generators, some microphones, and some electronic equipment. When magnetized, a watch will not keep time. For use around strong magnetic fields, watches should be specially protected with stainless-steel cases, and inner shields of a nickel alloy called Mu-metal under the dials and in back of the cases. Such watches provide protection against magnetic fields of 200 gauss. By comparison, the magnetic field of a telephone is of the order of about 8 gauss.

Some radical changes are on the horizon in watch construction. In the future, practically all watch cases (other than for some small ladies' watches) will be water- and dustproof. This will make possible the full advantages of oilless watches. Timekeeping is impaired not so much by oil losing its viscosity, but by becoming thickened by dust. It has been found that if the mainspring is highly polished, oil or grease between the coils is unnecessary. This feature has already been introduced into some watches. The advantage here lies in eliminating the difficulties which come from using the wrong kind of grease, or the wrong amount, when a watch is serviced. Watches have already been made with a material such as Teflon, instead of synthetic rubies as "jewels." This remarkable material, which can be made as hard as steel, feels sleazy to the touch. If you attempt to tighten your fingers hard on a piece, it simply slides away. When used as a bearing, it eliminates the necessity for oil. Oil congeals and stiffens with extreme cold. This is a major problem with aviators' watches. Teflon is unaffected by any temperatures which might be experienced. The combination of a permanently waterproof case and no oil will result in a watch which should run indefinitely without attention.

This revolution will not be achieved overnight, but will help the watch industry to cope with one of its major problems—the growing shortage of adequate servicemen against the continually increasing number of watches in use. Today's fine watches need regular cleaning and reoiling to maintain their efficiency. Small ladies' watches should be cleaned at least once a year; men's watches, at least every two years. Few people bother. Without such care, the life of any watch is materially shortened.

Another innovation is the elimination of the balance screws on the balance wheel. These were first added to permit a better adjustment of watches for temperature. They also permitted correction of deficiencies in uniformity in mass. The new alloys, from which balances are now made, are relatively un-

Evolution of the Man's Strap Watch. The earliest models of a half century ago were actually small pocket watches with attachments. Notice the seconds dial in the three o'clock position. The second watch down is of the World War I period. The strenuous efforts of watchmakers to pull out of the great depression of 1932 resulted in the creation of many bizarre and short-lived styles such as the rectangular watch at the bottom.

affected by temperature. Modern techniques have made it possible to generate a perfect circle from metal. Modern metals have a greatly improved uniformity. The screwless balance has the advantage of greater effective weight with equal outside diameter (or equal weight in a smaller size). As with other radical changes in watch construction, old-timers are "agin 'em."

The enormous progress which has been made in the alloys of metals in recent years will undoubtedly be increasingly utilized in the watch industry. None of the changes which are being made can be presumed to make possible watches of greater accuracy. The limit in that direction has been achieved in the best grade of production watches. They should enhance the quality of watches of lower price, and improve the quality of the very low priced watches.

What the watch industry needs, however, more than mechanical improvements, is a change of style comparable to the switch from pocket and chatelaine watches to wrist watches. When some genius, or set of circumstances, makes the wrist watch old-fashioned, the watch industry can start anew to supply the world with watches in the mode of the moment. Shakespeare probably said it first: "The fashion wears out more apparel than the man." Fashion must play an ever-increasing role in maintaining the health of the watch industry.

Back of pocket watch is portrait of Napoleon I,
framed in golden beads.
French, nineteenth century.

CHAPTER XI

The Testing of Watches

The Meridian Sundial

AS LATE AS 1700, most watches were still made with a single hand—the hour hand—and a watch that did not gain or lose more than an hour a day was considered to be an excellent timepiece. The fact that sun noon and clock noon only correspond on four days of the year was not known until the pendulum clock made its appearance. Universally, clocks and watches were set to time with a sundial at the moment of noon. Some sundials were constructed to show true sun noon with considerable accuracy, thus merely compounding the actual errors of the timepieces with which they were compared. Sundials for this purpose were usually mounted on a wall, since the information desired was the transit of the sun over the local meridian. In 1778, the first compensated meridian sundial designed to show corrected true clock noon according to the equation of time mentioned in Chapter IV, was erected on the south wall of St. Pierre Cathedral in Geneva. On a long arm extending at right angles to the wall there was a circular metal plate with a small hole in the center. The plate was parallel with the angle of true north. On the wall plate was a vertical line representing the meridian. The corrected noon time was represented by an elongated figure *8* imposed over the meridian line. The spot of sunlight successively traced this figure during the year, and clock noon could be determined with an accuracy of a few seconds. This became the time standard for the watchmakers of the town. The figure *8* scale of the equation of time, called an analemma, is used on some large globes, and is shown near the 180th meridian in the southern hemisphere.

That this compensated meridian sundial was put to good use is indicated by the organization of the first accuracy competition for ordinary watches. This was organized by the Society of Arts in Geneva in 1790. A prize of 20 louis d'or was offered for an ordinary watch which would not gain or lose more than one minute a day. Nineteen watches were entered in the competition, and tested for two months in two positions. Unfortunately, none qualified for the prize.

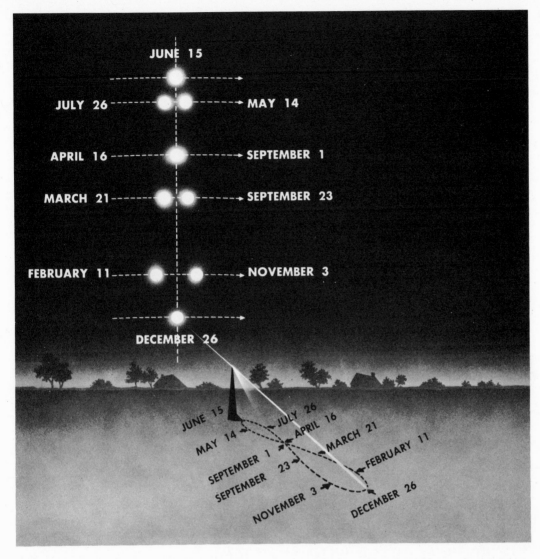

Analemma. The vertical diagram shows the relative altitude and position of the sun with respect to the meridian according to mean solar time. The elongated figure 8, the analemma, shows the path that would be traced by the shadow of a solid disk mounted on a vertical gnomon. This is the principle of the compensated meridian sundial erected on St. Pierre Cathedral in Geneva in 1778 by which mean noon could be determined within an accuracy of a few seconds. For such accuracy the analemma needs be some 10 feet high.

These watches, however, had no jewels which at this period were only used in England, and they did not have the anchor escapement which, though invented by Mudge in 1765, did not commonly appear in watches until around 1820.

The Beginning of Observatory Trials

The Geneva Observatory, founded in 1773, moved into a new building in 1829, and offered its facilities for the testing of watches. In 1853, it passed 28 marine chronometers; in 1874, 252. The usual period of the tests was 30 days.

In 1858, the Neuchâtel Observatory was founded with the announced purpose of lending its facilities to encourage the manufacture of watches of greater precision. Regular competitions for chronometers were begun in 1865, and have been continued ever since. Competitions were begun by the Geneva Observatory in 1870.

Kew-Teddington Physical Laboratory, associated with Greenwich Observatory which occupies the same relationship as our National Bureau of Standards to the United States Naval Observatory, began competitive accuracy competitions around 1887. The Naval Observatory at Washington inaugurated international accuracy competitions for chronometers in 1906, but discontinued them after 1924. The National Bureau of Standards continued to test watches until 1957, when this service was discontinued except for timepieces for some special and important use. The yearly competitions of Geneva, Neuchâtel, and Kew-Teddington have proved to be the most stimulating factor in the gradual improvement in the precision of timepieces, and today permit the entry of all types of timepieces—marine chronometers, deck watches (large pocket watches), pocket watches, and wrist watches. These various types of timepieces, however, do not compete on even terms—the larger the timepiece, the greater the handicap. Direct comparison of the results achieved by a wrist watch and a marine chronometer cannot be made.

The method of testing chronometers and watches has been greatly improved over the years. At first, as we have seen, the compensated meridian sundial permitted determinations with an accuracy of two to three seconds at noon. Then, accurate pendulum clocks were the standard. In later years, the standard was what is called a recording observatory chronograph.

The Recording Observatory Chronograph

This has a tuning-fork oscillator as a standard frequency, which drives a synchronous motor which, in turn, pulls a paper tape marked with graduations indicating seconds, tenths, and hundredths of seconds. Over the paper tape is an electrically actuated pen, controlled by a hand push switch, or telegraph key. The observer, using a magnifying glass, closes the switch when the second hand is straight up, or at "zero," causing the pen to make a mark on the tape. The amount that the watch is fast or slow can be determined to 0.01 second. It can easily be imagined that as the observer gets fatigued, repeating this operation time after time for any considerable period, the possibility of error is always present. Today, most observatories use a method developed by Kew-Teddington Laboratory, by which the passage of the second hand is automatically recorded by a photoelectric cell relay.

The leading watch manufactures of the world take proper pride in the performance of their timepieces in the observatory accuracy competitions. It is a general rule that watches submitted for trial be examples of regular production, and identified by a proper manufacturing serial number. While the timepieces are not specially built for the competition, they are very carefully *regulated*. Though all parts are standard, even in the best manufacturing techniques there are always minute variations, and any part that is in any particular substandard is replaced. Particular attention is paid to the tension and weight of springs, and the perfection and poise of the balance. The watches are then run for many months, and retouched from time to time, until no further improvement can be made. In this connection, it is interesting to note that a wrist watch of finest quality does not run its best when new, and must be kept running sometimes for as long as five years before it reaches peak performance. The parts are so small that the inevitable small imperfections due to machine fabrication introduce a roughness in the action that is gradually eliminated as the parts become polished through continued use. This is one of the major differences between a very fine modern wrist watch and one of ordinary grade. The fine watch improves with use and often is better after running ten years, than when new. The cheaper watch, being less finely made, becomes loose with wear, and accuracy deteriorates.

The "regulators" who prepare the watches for the competitions are highly skilled mechanics with years of experience, and special prizes are set up for them in the competitions. The name of the regulator is submitted with each watch entered, and he is thus given credit for the performance of the watches he prepared. One might well compare the regulator to the trainer of a race horse. A good trainer gets the best results from a good horse, as the regulator does from a good watch. Both would be helpless without the best material to start with. Just as the offspring of a champion command high prices, the products of a factory which can produce champions in observatory accuracy competitions can be logically regarded as superior products. The results of these competitions are published by the observatory, and are reprinted by many horological magazines. In these competitions, all watches entered are given a short preliminary test. It is sometimes like the qualifying runs which precede, for example, the 500-mile Indianapolis Race. About two-thirds of the watches entered fail in this preliminary trial.

Rating Watch Performance

The results of observatory trials are usually expressed in "marks" which are determined by complicated formulas. Efforts are now being made to have all observatories employ the same formulas, but at this moment they are all different and, for that reason, a direct comparison cannot be made between the score at one observatory and another. For general testing purposes, however, each has a published list of tolerances which must be met in order to receive classification.

Those of Kew-Teddington are most clearly stated. To receive a Class A certificate, a watch is tested for 44 days, divided into 8 periods. In each period, determination of the rate of the watch is made on consecutive days, and the rate is determined over a period of 24 hours. In order to provide for temperature changes, periods IV, V, VI, and VII are preceded by an intermediate day on which the rate of the watch is not taken.

PERIOD	APPROXIMATE TEMPERATURE	POSITION OF THE WATCH
I	67° F.	In the initial vertical position*
II	67° F.	Same, but turned clockwise 90°
III	67° F.	Same, but turned counterclockwise 90°
IV	42° F.	Horizontal position, dial up
V	67° F.	" " " "
VI	92° F.	" " " "
VII	67° F.	Horizontal position, dial down
VIII	67° F.	Initial vertical position

* Note: The initial vertical position is defined as follows:
  A. Pendant up, in the case of pocket watches.
  B. 6:00 o'clock up, in the case of wrist watches.
  C. 12:00 o'clock up, in the case of other watches.

A Class A certificate is issued:

1. If in each individual period of the test, the average departure of the 5 daily rates from the mean rate does not exceed 2 seconds a day.
2. If the mean rate in the initial vertical position (Periods I and VIII) differs from that in dial up position (Period V) by less than 5 seconds a day, and from that in any other position by less than 10 seconds per day.
3. If the mean change of rate with change of temperature is less than 0.3 second per day per 1° F.
4. If in each period (I, II, III, V, VII, and VIII) the mean rate does not exceed 10 seconds per day.

Marks are awarded for:

1. Consistency of rate from day to day (maximum 40 marks).
2. Consistency of rate with change of position (maximum 40 marks).
3. Consistency of rate with change of temperature (maximum 20 marks).

When a watch obtains 80 marks out of a possible total of 100, it is endorsed *particularly good.*

It can be seen that consistency of performance is what distinguishes an excellent watch. A watch that gains one day and loses the next is worthless. If the watch consistently gains a small amount, and these small amounts are relatively the same from day to day, one always knows where he stands with time, never worries about making dates or catching trains, and thereby avoids a lot of strain on both heart and disposition. One example of calculation for the initial period of the Kew-Teddington Class A test shows the results which must be obtained:

> The daily rate for five consecutive days was: plus 5.3, 6.9, 3.1, 2.5, and 3.5 seconds; the mean rate for the five days, plus 4.3 seconds. The daily *variations* from the mean rate were thus: 1.0, 2.6, 1.2, 1.8, and 0.8 seconds. The *mean variation* of the rate for the period was 1.48 seconds per day. The last figure is not an extraordinary performance. A wrist watch in the same test has shown a mean variation as little as .07 (7/100th) of a second.

The testing of wrist watches was begun by Neuchâtel Observatory in 1940. Preceding the formal opening of classes for wrist watches, the Observatory made an extensive comparison between results achieved in the laboratory tests and results shown by wearing on the wrist. This comparison showed that the different results achieved by several watches in the tests were repeated when worn on the wrist, and that the over-all performance of wrist watches when worn was substantially the same as recorded in the laboratory.

There is still another test given to watches such as navigational chronometers and chronographs used for precise timing of short intervals, as in sports timing. This is the test for isochronism. Isochronous means of equal intervals. With a timepiece that was perfectly isochronous, every hour, every minute, and every second would be exactly alike. In marine chronometers of the highest grade, this is very closely achieved. In ordinary watches, it is very seldom closely approached, and it is not of great importance. If a wrist watch in the course of a day is 5 seconds fast at one point, and 25 seconds fast at another, and 10 seconds slow at still another point, and averages out to be 10 seconds fast over 24 hours, it is good enough for anyone.

These variations in running, variations in isochronism, are largely the result of variations in the power of the mainspring, which in turn causes variations in the amplitude of motion of the balance. Such variations in power are always present. To measure them, the U. S. Bureau of Standards has developed an automatic recorder of watch beats which, over a period of 24 hours, produces a graph showing momentary variations in time. In principle, it resembles somewhat the electronic watch testers used by many jewelers. With such a test for isochronism, one can see how it is possible for a timing watch to have an error in a period of 15 seconds, which is many times greater than would be indicated by its total daily error for 24 hours. "What," some watchmakers may say, "can be the error in fifteen seconds, when the daily error for twenty-four hours is only twenty seconds—why, you couldn't even measure it!" The fact is that due to variations in mainspring power, such a watch can show a very considerable error—as much as 0.5 second for a period of 15 seconds. Observatory tests for timing watches begin with 1 second, and are continued progressively for 10 seconds, and then at 5-second intervals to 30 seconds, and then at 15-second intervals to 5 minutes, then at 1-minute intervals to 1 hour. Each test includes starting and stopping the watch. There is an error, however small, in each period. In the finest one-tenth second timing watch, it rarely exceeds 0.1 second plus or minus, anywhere. In a cheap timing watch, it can amount to as much as 0.7 second in 15 seconds, and the trouble is that the occurrence of the errors is unpredictable.

Complicated movement of split-second chronograph.

CHAPTER XII

Complicated and Special Purpose Watches

A Complication Defined

WHEN ANYTHING is added to a watch to perform a special function, it is, in watchmaking parlance, a complication. Only the best—and that means the most expensive—complicated watches are worth buying, if the complication is added to the function of telling time of day. To buy a cheap complicated watch is looking for trouble.

Wrist Alarm Watches

Alarm watches, which have been made for centuries, are growing in popularity in modern wrist-watch form. They serve the useful purpose of reminding the wearer of important things to be done at certain times during the day. Strangely enough, they attract both very meticulous people and very forgetful ones. The alarm can be set to ring at any desired time with an accuracy of about 5 minutes. A separate alarm spring usually sounds the alarm for 15 to 20 seconds, but can be stopped at will. The spring must be rewound after each use. The alarm makes a buzzing sound which is not audible a few feet away, but sufficient to alert the wearer. Ladies' alarm watches are made to be carried in purse or handbag.

Chronographs

A chronograph is a time-of-day watch, to which has been added a stop-watch mechanism. A *plain* chronograph has an independent sweep second hand which can be started, stopped, and returned to zero by successive pressure on the stem. It usually has an independent minute register, which counts the number of revolutions of the second hand up to 30 minutes. When the second hand is returned to zero, the minute register is also cleared. Chronograph mechanisms are usually added to a watch with a 5-beat escapement, and the space between the second markings is divided into fifths of seconds.

The first chronograph was made by Jean-Moyes Pouzait in 1776. This was known as a "dead seconds" watch, and provision was made to stop the second hand, but it was started again from this position. In 1861, Henri-Féréol Piquet added a mechanism which permitted the second hand to be returned to zero after being stopped. Chronograph watches in much their present form have been made since 1885, but in recent years, have been substantially improved —particularly in the direction of accuracy.

The time-out chronograph is the next in increased complication. This has two pushpieces, one to start and stop the second hand, the other to return it to zero. By this means, any number of separate time intervals can be accumulated and added up. In games such as football, basketball, and hockey, where time-out is taken, this is the watch used.

The third complication is the use of two center second hands—one mounted over the other. One hand is called the sweephand, the other the split, from which comes its name, split-second chronograph. After the two hands are started by pressure on the stem, for example, a pressure on a side pushpiece stops the split-hand while the sweephand continues, permitting the time to be read from the splithand at this interval. After the time has been read, a second push on the side pushpiece causes the splithand to jump to join its moving mate, and the two hands again proceed as one. This is a favorite watch with race-track followers and horse trainers, since it permits the time to be taken at the quarter, the half, and the three-quarter, and still get the time at the finish. In track events, one can count the time of laps, and also time the finish of two contestants, getting one on the split, and the other on the sweep. This watch has the usual minute register.

Still another complication is added when both hands of the split-second chronograph can be stopped and started for time-out.

Plain and time-out chronographs are made in both pocket and wrist types. While split-second chronographs have been made in wrist size, they are rarely seen. The pocket variety is expensive enough.

These timing functions are also available in watches which do not show the time of day. They are called plain timers, time-out timers, and split-second timers. There are two types commonly sold: those with continuously running movements where starting and stopping is caused by the meshing of gears; and proper stop watches, where the whole movement starts and stops with the second hand. The first type is more expensive and more accurate. The latter is inexpensive and durable, but not very accurate. These timers can be had to measure fifths, tenths, twenty-fifths, fiftieths, or hundredths of a second. In all these watches, there is a center timing wheel with 300 teeth, on which the second hand is mounted. When driven by a 5-beat watch, it makes one revolution in 60 seconds (5 into 300 equals 60); with a 10-beat watch, one revolution in 30 seconds; a 25-beat watch, one revolution in 12 seconds; a 50-beat watch, one revolution in 6 seconds; a 100-beat watch, one revolution in 3 seconds. In these watches, the balance wheel actually oscillates at the rates noted. Obviously, the running time of these watches is rapidly reduced as the beat is increased. A watch with a 40-hour mainspring will run only 20 hours at 10 beats per second; a hundredth second watch, only 2 hours, theoretically, but actually much less.

The Cost of Accuracy

As has been mentioned previously, the accuracy of timing watches is almost directly related to isochronism. A split-second pocket chronograph with time-out feature, carefully made for relatively perfect isochronism cannot be purchased for much less than $500 retail, in a plain nickel case. Similar chronographs, in 14- or 18-carat gold cases, have been sold for $1,000 to $2,000. A tenth-second, split-second timer with comparable accuracy, good enough to get a timing certificate from a national observatory, justifies a price of $350 as just about the minimum. These prices can serve as a guide with which to measure the accuracy and reliability of lower-priced timing watches.

For industrial use, or for photography, radio, television, and motion pictures, where time to less than a second is not calculated, less costly timers are sufficiently accurate. In the measurement of a series of say, ten time intervals, the aggregate error would probably be about a second.

In the timing of a championship sports event, where world-renown can be earned by bettering a previous record by 0.1 second, only the finest watch, certified by an observatory certificate not over six months old, should be used, but at the present time this has not been put in the rules, except for Olympic events. Many sports records can be looked at askance, unless the previous record was beaten decisively.

Reaction Time

This is a good place to correct a commonly held opinion concerning reaction time, and the probable errors inherent in timing with hand-held watches. This opinion is largely the result of published figures concerning the reaction time of automobile drivers. Many of these tests were made under the sponsorship of the American Automobile Association by several universities. The tests involve the complex reaction to certain common highway signals, such as: green light, red light, and left- and right-turn arrows, to which the test driver was to respond by appropriate use of the steering wheel, brake, accelerator, or clutch. The reaction time taken from the average time for a series of tests varied from subject to subject, from 0 seconds to 0.850 second. The average among men subjects was 0.593 second; for women, 0.668 second. The effect of age was negligible up to thirty, but after that there was an increase of about 0.01 second for each two years of age. However, some subjects at seventy had a reaction time equal to that of the average of the twenty-year-olds.

It is obvious that the tripping of a timing watch is a vastly different problem. First, the reaction is that to an *expected* event—the timer knows that in a second or two a runner is going to cross before his eyes, and he is ready. In the second place, instead of struggling with the mental complication of deciding what move he is to make, whether of steering wheel, clutch, brake, or accelerator, he simply has to press his index finger a small fraction of an inch. With the best timers, the reaction time is virtually zero. I have seen four out of six timers, using certified watches, clock a sixty-yard dash or high-hurdle race right at the exact same tenth of a second, and the time was exactly the same to 0.1 second compared with an electronic timer of the highest precision. Repeated tests of this kind show that first-class manual timing usually does not vary more than 0.04 second from the best quartz clock, electrically operated. This does not mean to say that all men acting as official timers are first class. Many are not. Their biggest fault is failure to concentrate, or inattention, and lack of practice. Triggering a timing watch is almost identical with target shooting. One must press the trigger at exactly the moment when on target. It is easier than target shooting in that there is no gun to hold steady; but the principle is the same.

Types of Chronograph Dials

Chronographs are made with many types of dials. One is the tachometer dial, which shows the speed of, for instance, a car when traveling over a measured course of a mile or a kilometer. The second hand is started at the beginning of the mile and stopped at the end. The speed in miles per hour is then read on the tachometer scale. Another is the telemeter scale, which was very useful in earlier days, to artillery gunners. The watch was started when the flash of the enemy's gun was seen, and stopped when the sound was heard. The scale showed the distance of the enemy's gun. This is measuring the difference in the speed of light and sound. A telemeter scale can also be used to tell how far away a lightning bolt fell. The watch is started at the flash, and stopped at the peal of thunder; then the distance is read on the scale. When simultaneous radio and sound beacons were first installed on lighthouses and lightships, many ships ran into them when following the radio beacon in a pea-soup fog. To avoid this danger, special watches were made with telemeter dials in nautical miles. The captain could then tell his distance by starting the watch when the radio signal was heard, and stopping it when the sound signal reached him. Today, the radio beacon dies out within a mile or so from its source, and the ship, forewarned, can change course accordingly.

Still another scale sometimes found on chronograph watches is known as the pulsimeter, which is useful to physicians. Starting with the second hand straight up, the scale shows the pulse rate per minute when 30 pulse beats have been counted. This system has never become standard practice with doctors and nurses.

For the use of aviators, there are wrist chronographs with both a 60-minute register, and a 12-hour register. This is useful for counting elapsed time of a flight.

Aircraft mostly employ clock-type chronographs, or timers, mounted on the instrument panel. During blind flight, these are relied upon to bring the plane safely to ground. Approaching the airport, the pilot has (depending on air speed) between two minutes and one minute before touchdown after he picks up the I.L.S. (instrument landing system) and turns on his panel timer. Usually 12 seconds before touchdown, he will reach the point of decision, at which time his plane should be 200 feet in the air, and 3,500 feet from the end of the runway. If he has broken out of the overcast when this point is reached, he can glide on into a landing; if not, he must follow a prescribed missed approach procedure, and go around again.

Other timers on aircraft record hours in the air, or of operation, and automatically turn on and off when the motors are started or stopped, thus showing the 1,000 hours, or whatever the period should be before the motors need overhaul. Private plane owners use an ordinary time-out timer for the same purpose, starting and stopping it manually.

The number of complications which can be put on a watch are endless, but as mentioned at the beginning of this Chapter, each complication adds to initial cost, and cost of upkeep. You can buy for $4,500 the most complicated of all. It shows time of day, it is a split-second chronograph, it shows the day of the week, the date, and the year, all automatically (even compensating for leap years), and it shows the phases of the moon. It is also a minute-repeater which rings out the time, when a tiny button is pressed. This magnificent timepiece costs about $200 to have cleaned.

A strap chronograph usually costs about $25 to clean and reoil. There is an enormously complicated timing watch used by some sports car drivers, which costs at least $50 to service. If one can afford to drive an expensive automobile this should seem a trifle, but such is not human nature. The main problem in the maintenance of complicated watches is not the *cost* of service, but finding someone really experienced in the work. If the work is attempted by a careless or inexperienced mechanic, too bad!

To buy a chronograph wrist watch to wear as an ornament just because you like the looks of it is an expensive luxury, unless you can afford the upkeep. If you do occasional timing, buy an inexpensive pocket stop watch for this purpose, and wear a conventional wrist watch. Inexpensive stop watches, accurate to a second, are rugged, and often will go for years without attention. This is, of course, quite the reverse for a high-precision timing watch, which is expected to measure time accurately to 0.2 or 0.1 second.

Calendar Watches

Calendar wrist watches are useful to many. One type just shows the date of the month. Since they register 31 days, they require adjustment for 30-day months, and for the month of February. Other calendar watches show also the month and the day of the week. Some show the phases of the moon—approximately. Some moon-phase watches have been set to correspond with menstrual periods.

Chronograph dials showing: C, 1/5 second divisions; D, minute recorder; E, three-minute divisions; F, hour recorder; Q, tachometer scale; S, pulsimeter scale.

CHAPTER XIII

Electricity and Time

The Great Illusion

MANY PEOPLE THINK that the household electric clock is always right. For household affairs, this is substantially true. You can usually get correct time to the approximate minute from most household electric clocks.

But, for precise time to the second, the electric clock is not consistently a reliable authority. Electric clocks are powered by alternating current (A.C.), which reverses 60 times per second in most United States cities. In Europe, 50-cycle A.C. current is usually delivered by power companies. The voltage, nominally 110 or 220, has no effect on timekeeping if the clock is made for current of the voltage supplied. We can think of 60-cycle A.C. current as a balance wheel of a watch oscillating at that rate. The accuracy obviously depends on the frequency being maintained at a constant 60 per second. It is not commercial practice to produce pure 60-cycle A.C. electricity for power purposes. The frequency varies fractionally from 60 cycles, and as it varies, the clock must run either fast or slow accordingly. "But," you say, "my clock doesn't; it's always right." It always *appears* to be right because at intervals during the day the power company speeds up or slows down the frequency of the current to correct any deficiency which may have occurred. An error of three or four seconds or more one way or the other passes without notice. In the home, seconds hardly count.

Electric motors of the form used in clocks have been made for many years. The "invention" of the electric clock, or the thing that made relative accuracy possible, was a change in the method of power transmission around 1920, through which a much closer frequency could be maintained. While not pure 60-cycle, the variations are small enough to be readily compensated. If you question a powerhouse engineer about variations in frequency, he will reply, "Sir, we do not sell a time service." However, most power companies do very well as far as the needs of a household clock are concerned.

Hundreds of types of battery-powered household clocks have been designed and marketed over the years, with indifferent success. Batteries create power as the result of chemical change. The rate is not constant, but tends to fall off with time. The chemical action is faster when hot, and slower when cold. Since the battery cannot be used as a self-governing source of power, a governor in the form of a pendulum, or balance wheel, must be introduced, and we end up with a clockwork to which we have added the complications of electricity and chemistry to those of the clock itself.

As these lines are written, electric watches are on the horizon. These appear to be of two types: one, a small battery, which is used to wind the mainspring of the watch; and two, the use of magnetic coils to keep the balance wheel in motion, and thus, an electric "escapement." The driving force in this case is the balance wheel which, through gears, causes the hands of the watch to jump forward with each oscillation. With the rapid advances in microchemistry and electronics, it is possible that a truly electronic watch may one day be made and have its day, but the combination of small size, good accuracy, low maintenance, and relatively low cost of the mechanical watch, presents a challenge of some magnitude. Experimental models of an actual electronic man's wrist watch have been made and they run with great accuracy. The model contains a highly miniaturized tuning fork of special design, a transistor, battery, and a few gears. The problem of producing this watch in quanities, at a price to compete with conventional mechanical watches is formidable, though probably not impossible. At this moment the idea of further reducing the components to the size required for a small ladies' watch seems unthinkable.

Electronic Clocks

For scientific use, electronic clocks have been created which, for short periods (a few years), have performed with a degree of accuracy surpassing the best mechanical timepieces.

The basic principle involves the design of an electronic circuit which will generate a relatively pure alternating current of a specific frequency. A governor, one might say, is then put astride this frequency to stabilize it, and keep it within narrow limits of the exact frequency desired. These governors are of two common types—the tuning fork, and the quartz crystal. A tuning fork, as is well known, will vibrate and emit a definite tone when struck. The tone is due to the frequency of the vibrations, which in turn is controlled by the size, mass, and density of the material used in the fork. A above middle C of a piano in the United States is the result of vibrations at the rate of 440 per second. When very carefully made, a tuning fork will vibrate at a very precise frequency. A quartz crystal, when subjected to pressure, will "vibrate," and in so doing will produce a feeble electric current with a frequency depending on the size, shape, and structure of the crystal. While the vibrations of the tuning fork are within audible, or sound levels, those of most quartz crystals used in clocks are commonly in the supersonic range of 100,000 per second. Both the tuning fork and quartz crystal are influenced by temperature and atmospheric pressure, and must be housed in "ovens" at a temperature substantially higher than that in which they are used, and sealed in partial vacuum.

The current controlled by these electric governors is amplified electronically, and divided to produce a pure A.C. of the desired frequency. The final apparatus is known as an oscillator, or a frequency standard. Both have been used to operate clocks. A common use of the tuning-fork oscillator is in the "Watchmaster," which is used by watch repairers to check watch performance.

The accuracy of these devices depends on the perfection of all of the components. A quartz-crystal oscillator can be purchased for, say, $200. However, a quartz clock suitable for use in an observatory involves a cost of several thousand dollars, and as much as $100,000 has been spent to achieve close to the ultimate in accuracy. As an example, only three or four of a hundred "perfect" crystals measure up to observatory standards, and to select these represents a year or more of testing. When carried to the ultimate in perfection, some observatory clocks have run with a calculated accuracy of 0.002 second per year, but to achieve this accuracy, they must have the careful daily supervision of experts.

The Ammonia Clock

Still further refinement in timekeeping has been achieved with the ammonia clock, in which the natural vibrations of the molecules of ammonia serve as the final governor. This molecule is made up of three hydrogen atoms and one nitrogen atom. When a radio wave is passed through ammonia gas, the nitrogen atoms vibrate at a frequency of 23,870 megacycles. When the output of a quartz-crystal oscillator is converted into radio waves at this frequency, and passed through the ammonia gas, any variation from the precise frequency of 23,870 per second is corrected by the tube of ammonia gas which acts as an added governor. The accuracy of these clocks defies the usual to-the-second comparison, and is stated mathematically. A watch with an error of two seconds per day can be described as having an error of one part in 86,400. The ammonia clock at the United States Bureau of Standards in Washington is stable to one part to one hundred million, and ammonia clocks have been built with a calculated error of two parts per billion!

The Atomic Clock

A still further improvement has been achieved with the atomic clock, on which vibrations of cesium atoms serve as the master governor of the frequency

Cesium beam atomic clock, one of two atomic clocks in operation at the National Bureau of Standards, Washington, D.C. It has a potential accuracy of one part in ten billion, which is about equal to an error of one second in 300 years. In the beam tube illustrated above, cesium metal which is liquid at room temperature is converted into a gas by an electric furnace. The tube also contains two magnetic filters between which the stream of cesium atoms is exposed to a radio field kept tuned closely to their natural frequency of vibration of 9,192,632 cycles per second by a precision quartz clock. If this radio frequency is not precisely correct, the cesium atoms fail to get through the second magnetic filter, and this actuates a mechanism which corrects the frequency of the quartz clock. The frequency of the quartz clock after correction is amplified and, if desired, can be divided and used to operate a precision electric clock telling time of day. Atomic clocks have taken over from astronomers the measurements of intervals of time less than one month.

of a precise quartz crystal clock, as is done in the ammonia clock. Cesium is a metal which, like mercury, is liquid at room temperature. Its atom has a natural period of vibration of 9,192,632 cycles per second. The utilization of the vibrations of the cesium atom to drive a clock has resulted in an accuracy of one part in ten billion, which is equivalent to an error of one second in 300 years. Commercial cesium "clocks" are available at $500,000 each, and weigh

500 pounds. These are not true clocks, and their use is in generating precise frequencies with which to measure the accuracy of other frequencies. Since the tube in which the cesium atoms are made to work has a life of only about 1,000 hours, it obviously is only for intermittent use as a measuring tool.

Another development, known as the Maser clock (for microwave amplification by stimulated emission of radiation), uses the ammonia molecule in an excited state as the source of the emission of a frequency, rather than as a governor. An accuracy of one part in ten billion has been produced, and still the search goes on. The uses of these superaccurate "timepieces" is set forth in Chapter XIV.

Timing a Light Beam. New tool for field survey work is the Geodimeter developed by the Swedish scientist Dr. Erik Bergstrand. A pulsating pencil of light is reflected back to a sensitive photocell on the instrument from a point as remote as 30 miles distant. The time between a light pulse and return establishes the unknown distance. A timing method of phase comparison is made by special electronic techniques. A distance of one mile, during which the light beam travels from instrument to reflector and back in 10 millionths of a second, can be measured within an instrumental error of less than 4 inches. With the Geodimeter the speed of light has been measured as 186,282.2 miles per second.

The Future of Time

From Ancient Beliefs

UNTIL THE BEGINNING of the scientific revolution, around 1500, the conception of the universe remained much as Aristotle had described it some eighteen centuries earlier. Fixed in space, in its center was our earthly globe, made of four elements: earth, fire, water, and air. Around it were eleven spheres, one within the other, composed of the perfect quintessence, a celestial material not found on earth. Fixed to the first sphere was the moon, and then in expanding order, Mercury, Venus, the Sun, Mars, Jupiter, and Saturn. Beyond these was the sphere of the firmament, to which was fastened the fixed stars; the Crystalline Heaven; the *primum mobile;* and finally, the Empyraean Heaven, "the abode of the Gods and all the elect." The *primum mobile,* the prime mover of the heavens, imparted motion to the whole system which revolved from east to west in exactly twenty-four hours.

The conception was simple, neat, and tidy. "Timed by the Stars," as an advertising claim for watches, is still considered meaningful and convincing.

The great scientific achievements, from Aristotle to Einstein, put us in mind of the remark of a great English physicist, that each new discovery but expands the frontiers of ignorance. The more that is learned about the vastness of the starry heavens, the more complex become the problems still to be solved. Each new advance in the precision of timepieces appears to have complicated the difficulties of using astronomical observations as the final time reference.

Some seventy years ago, it became suspected that the rotation of the earth could no longer be considered as the basis for an invariable time standard. With observations of the sun, moon, and planets, this suspected phenomenon was proved, although the reasons still are not well understood.

The Earth Is Slowing Down

According to Dr. G. M. Clemence, Director of the *Nautical Almanac* of the United States Naval Observatory, a clock keeping perfect time would have been 2.6 hours slow 2,000 years ago; about 1750, it would have been on time; in 1850, 2 seconds slow; in 1900, 3.9 seconds fast; in 1940, 24.9 seconds slow. It also now appears that the rotation of the earth is slowing down at a rate to produce a shortening of the mean solar day by about 0.001 second per century. (If this slowing down continues, in some millions of years, the earth will always turn the same face toward the sun, as the moon now does to the earth, and the day will equal about 47 of our present days!)

The New Astronomical Second

For scientific purposes, both in astronomy and physics, the basic time standard has been the mean solar second, representing 1/86,400th part of the mean solar day. The length of the mean solar day, to which we now set our clocks, was established around 1750. Some have disputed the apparent vagaries in the time of rotation of the earth, laying the supposed variations to errors in observation, rather than time. Nevertheless, it is now held that for short periods of less than a month, the quartz clock is a more exact time standard than observational astronomy.

At the General Assembly of the International Astronomical Union meeting in 1948, the question was raised as to the desirability of arriving at a new definition of the "legal" second. At its meeting in 1955, the decision was made. For astronomical purposes, the second was defined as 1/31,556,925.975 of the tropical year 1900.0, the 0 indicating the beginning of the year.

Use is made of this standard in the following manner. In accordance with the law of universal gravitation, if the position of the moon is known precisely at a particular instant, and if its speed and direction are also known for the same instant, then its position at any other time in the past or future can be calculated precisely. From the time of Newton, who propounded the gravitational theory, a number of astronomers have devoted their lives to the creation of lunar theories. The calculations involve millions of figures, and the work can be ruined by a single error at any stage. Today, predictions of the movement of the moon can be said to be precise. Such movements for the year 1900.0 have been confirmed. By yearly comparison between predicted motion and actual motion, any errors in time due to the rotation of the earth can be detected. Conclusions based on lunar observation can be confirmed by observations of the apparent movement of the planets and stars.

For the mundane affairs of everyday life, the clock, set to 1750 time, will still be the standard, although the astronomers have parted company with it, except as a source of reference. The physicist, at this time, is preparing to part company with the astronomical time standard in favor of one of his own. In his quest, the physicist faces problems comparable to the evolution of a new lunar theory. One of the projects of the International Geophysical Year (1957–1958) will be an attempt to more closely relate the new astronomical second of Ephemeris time to the second of the Uniform time kept by our clocks. For this purpose, twenty cameras placed around the world will accumulate a mass of additional data by recording observations of the moon.

Time and the Physicist

We cannot here solve the problems of the physicist, but the subject of time would be incomplete unless they were at least stated. The problem of the astronomers was to divide the year to find the second. That of the physicist is to divide the second to find a frequency.

The 92 natural elements have been reduced in present concepts of physics to a few fundamental particles in the structure of the atoms, and all natural forces are considered as varying manifestations of electromagnetic waves of different frequency and wave length. Light, heat, X ray, radio, television differ only through wave length and frequency.

In its perception of frequencies, the ear has a vastly greater capacity than the eye. The ear detects a range of ten octaves, the eye but one. Visible light occupies a narrow segment of the electromagnetic spectrum, beginning with violet and ending with red (as seen in a rainbow). With the color violet, the eye loses its sensitivity, and ultraviolet, X rays, gamma rays, and cosmic rays, which follow in the electromagnetic spectrum, must be "seen" by other methods. Red ends the visible spectrum; the infrared radiation which follows cannot be seen, but is felt as a sensation of heat. These are ultrashort waves, and after an unused blank comes the microwave radiation used in radar, followed by the waves used for broadcasting, television, communication, and others presently unknown.

The frequency and wave length of these various manifestations of electromagnetic waves have been determined for present practical purposes, using two assumptions: one, the length of the second; and two, the speed of light. Frequency is the number of electromagnetic waves which arrive at a given point in one second. Wave length multiplied by frequency equals the speed of light.

The Relation Between Length and Time

The problem is more than an abstract one in pure physics, and can be made clear by consideration of the present standard of length. It is not generally known that the legal standard of length in the United States is the meter, although its use is not compulsory. Feet, yards, and miles are defined as so many parts or numbers of meters. What is a meter? The meter was legalized by the French National Academy in 1791 as 0.0000001 part of a meridional quadrant of the earth, following a recommendation of the Paris Academy of Science. The prime, the Meter of the Archives, was made according to this formula, of platinum. It was legalized in 1875 by an international treaty known as the International Metric Convention, to which the United States was a party. Prototype copies of the Meter of the Archives were then made, and each of the signatory powers received one. It was later found that the calculations with respect to the length of a meridional quadrant were in error, and consequently the legal meter is related to nothing, other than the happenstance length of a prototype meter, which is reposing in the vault of the International Bureau of Weights and Measures in Sèvres, France, and which is the same length as the original Meter of the Archives of 1791. A prototype copy, made of 90 per cent platinum and 10 per cent iridium in the vault of the National Bureau of Standards at Washington, D.C., is the American standard of length.

The Bureau of Standards has a number of exact copies of its prototype standard meter, some subdivided into centimeters, but the problem of checking other scales or meters with them requires an enormous expenditure of time and care. In a word, the system lacks an important quality required of a research tool, and that is *availability*. This is one of the factors that has brought about a move to find a substitute for the meter bar. With the advances made in the sciences in recent years, it seems possible to utilize monochromatic light as a wave-length standard of length. For this purpose, the wave length of the red line of cadmium has been studied since 1892. The Bureau of Standards has proposed the wave length of the green radiation of the 198 isotope of mercury.

The Speed of Light

When one reads the statement that the velocity of light was *finally* and *accurately* determined as 186,284 miles per second in 1849, one wonders what was used as a time standard. But later estimates give 186,218 miles per second. While either estimate is sufficiently accurate for most purposes, most physicists believe that, with further work, a much closer estimate may be made. What is sought as a *physical constant* is the speed of light in vacuum. In one recent determination by the Bureau of Standards, use was made of two radio receivers set up exactly 1,500 meters apart. The distance was measured with geodetic tape, which in turn had been checked against the 5-meter standard of length kept by the Bureau. In computing the results, consideration had to be given to a number of factors, such as refractive index of the atmosphere, pressure, temperature, water-vapor content, effects of the ground, reflections from distant mountains, and others. A great number of determinations were made over many days, and the results were calculated with utmost precision. Beyond its theoretical value, the best possible determination of the speed of light will be of great practical importance in connection with the use of the Geodimeter, which is used extensively in geodetic surveying.

When agreement as to the speed of light has been reached, perhaps there will also be agreement as to the length of the second. Actually, what the physicist wants is less a standard of time than a standard of frequency. Present indications are that he will choose the vibrations of ammonia, or other atoms, as outlined in the previous Chapter where atomic clocks were discussed.

The measurement of the wave length of light, and some forms of radiation is expressed in angstrom units, or angstroms (Å), which is 0.1 millimicron, or 0.0001 micron, or 0.000,000,1 millimeter. Should the wave length of a monochromatic light be adopted as a new standard of length, it would be possible, by using the angstrom as the smallest unit, to arbitrarily set a new standard for an *optical* meter. The matter probably will not be resolved for years.

It appears certain, however, that an atomic standard of time will eventually be adopted in the physical sciences, and if it should be found that astronomical time is consistently slowing down with respect to atomic time, then a very important problem would be created. There is no branch of science, theoretical or applied, which is not concerned directly or indirectly with these unresolved questions.

It is interesting to note here that the idea of using a unit of time to determine a standard of length was proposed by the English watchmaker George Graham in 1742. He had found that a pendulum beating seconds in London measured exactly 39.13 of the then accepted inches. In 1758, an English standard yard was adopted with the length 36 inches determined with the pendulum as a measuring stick. In 1836, the pendulum standard was further refined by specifying the conditions under which the second pendulum was to function: temperature 62° F., operating in a vacuum, at sea level, and in London. With the refinements, the length of the pendulum was fixed at 39.1393 inches. This remained the legal standard of length in England until 1855. The English "yardstick," executed first in brass, and later in a bronze bar, was adopted by the United States, and was legal until it was replaced by the metric system in 1866.

Radar and Loran

The wartime invention of Loran (a contraction of Long Range Navigation) in 1941, first used in 1942 with fifty ships equipped with instruments, has since developed into a world-wide system, and constitutes one of the most important electronic aids to navigation. Loran's older brother is radar (a contraction of radio detecting and ranging), the first model of which was produced in 1937. Both involve the measurement of time in millionths of seconds (microseconds,

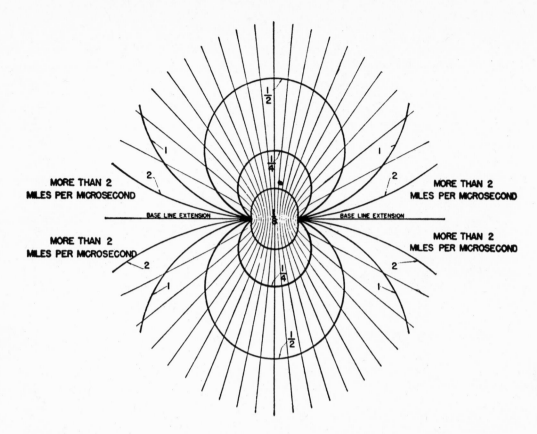

Accuracy of Loran Lines of Position. The numbers refer to the number of miles per microsecond time difference.

ms). Based on a figure of 186,218 miles per second as the speed of light and radio waves, a nautical mile is represented by a time of 6.18 microseconds.

Radar consists of a transmitter used as an oscillator emitting pulses of electromagnetic waves of extremely high frequency ranging from 3,000 to as high as 30,000 megacycles, which are transmitted from a highly directional antenna which also serves to receive the echo or bounce-back of the signal when it hits some object—for example, a ship, shore line, cloud. The distance between time of transmission and arrival of echo can be measured on the scale of the "scope," the face of a cathode-ray tube, and is calculated as 983 feet per microsecond. The short waves of radar travel in a straight line, and over land or water are restricted to the line of sight, due to the curvature of the earth. This restriction does not apply when radar is used from an airplane, or toward the sky.

Loran, which operates on a frequency just above those used for commercial broadcasting (1750–1950 kilocycles), has a range of up to about 700 miles by day, and about twice that by night. Like broadcast transmission, the waves both follow the curvature of the earth (the ground waves) and travel skyward. Here they strike the ionosphere, an area in the upper atmosphere that is ionized, or electrified by the ultraviolet radiation of the sun. This is not a solid belt, but consists of patches of ionized air, of which two layers have been

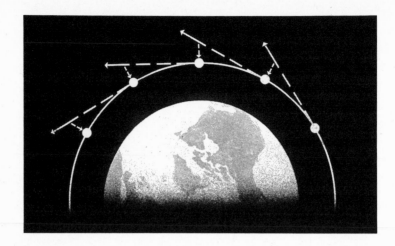

Time and the Earth Satellite. The speed of the satellite and the attraction of gravity keep the man-made moon in its orbit. The forward speed of 4.7 miles per second is countered by a gravitation pull equal to a fall of 14 feet in the same time. The release of second and third stage rockets and final ejection of the nose element with the satellite is controlled by timing devices which have to function perfectly under enormously difficult conditions in combination with intricate electro-mechanical instruments.

named. The Kennelly-Heaviside layer, 60 to 100 miles above the earth, reflects radio waves of frequencies up to 3,000 kilocycles; the Appleton layer, at a height of 120 to 300 miles, reflects shorter radio waves of higher frequencies. Both areas behave differently by day and night, at different seasons, and at different times during sunspot cycles.

The Loran system consists of transmitting stations on the ground, usually close to coast lines, and receivers located on ships or planes. Loran transmitters are set up in pairs, spaced from 200 to 400 or more miles apart, one of which is a master station, and the other a slave. Like radar, the Loran transmitters send out pulses. Identification of the transmitters is made by differences in the pulses, by time delays between master and slave stations, and by frequency of the transmission. Loran waves travel on great circle routes over the earth, which become hyperbolas when laid down on the usual marine chart.

The system is described in detail in the publication of the United States Hydrographic Office, known as "H. O. 205, *Radio Navigational Aids.*" The speed of the electromagnetic waves of Loran were found to vary markedly from the classic determination of the speed of light. Numerous Loran time measurements showed position contrary to the known position of the transmitting stations. The speed was shown to vary from about 140,000 miles per second to something less than 180,000 miles per second. Daytime ground-wave range extends to approximately 600 nautical miles in the Atlantic, and 800 in the Pacific. Sky-wave coverage, most usually used at night, extends to about 1,500 miles. The variation in time as compared to distance in Loran waves is somewhat analogous to compass variations. Today, navigators have available to them a series of Loran charts, which show the compensation which must be made for Loran readings over much of the northern portion of the globe.

The effect of the earth, its land and water areas, and its atmosphere, on the transmission of electromagnetic waves, both of radio and light, has been seen to be considerable. Before the launching of the first Sputnik, exploration of the upper air by means of rockets had indicated the presence of magnetic currents in rings or sheets which might have a profound effect on putting a satellite into orbit. The complex operation of altering the direction of a rocket from vertical to horizontal, or its orbit position, involves both radar observation and time measurements. The speed of radio transmission from the American satellites is more consistent as to time than was anticipated. This has permitted accurate calculations of their orbits. It may well prove that the assumption of the astronomers that the speed of light in outer space is approximately the same as that calculated for a vacuum will prove correct.

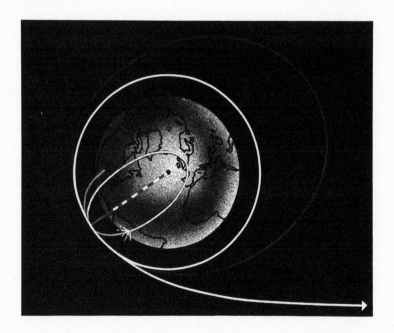

A Satellite May Be Lost. The speed of the earth satellite when put into orbit is critical. As speed at release increases, the satellite travels farther from point beneath launching. At 4.7 miles per second it circles. As its speed of launching increases, its orbit becomes a larger and larger ellipse. At 6.7 miles per second, it reaches speed of escape and leaves earth permanently. Man-made moons appear to travel across the sky at greater speed than any natural object because of nearness. They are photographed through special tracking telescopes by cameras making exposures at intervals controlled by a high-precision quartz clock.

Dr. William F. Meggers of the National Bureau of Standards positions the eyepiece of the optical train prior to observation of the circular interference fringes of green light from the electrodeless mercury 198 lamp (left foreground). *Length measurements based on this interference pattern* (background) *can be made with an accuracy of one part in one hundred million.*

This volume is closed with the observation that, in musing on history, one toys with the idea that nothing changes in the substance of things. The change is one of name, rather than function. Pure science, like pure art, is not profitable, and someone must subsidize the scientists and the artists. Yesterday it was Louis XIV who filled his palace with men of brains, skills, and spirit. Today it is the great corporations, with their research laboratories, or foundations created by industrialists, who encourage the thinkers, the philosophers, the dreamers, and the talented. But neither yesterday's crowned kings, nor today's kings of finance command the muse of discovery. In due time something better, or at least different, will be here. It is not for us to command, but to wait. A lifetime is but a fugitive second in the course of evolution.

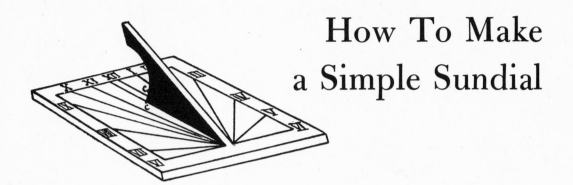

How To Make
a Simple Sundial

THE SIMPLEST FORM of sundial to construct is a horizontal dial. When mounted on a pedestal it becomes an attractive ornament for garden or lawn. Such a dial can be oriented to a true north and south position. A vertical wall sundial can be constructed in the same general way, providing the south wall of the house is substantially parallel to the north and south axis of the earth. By north and south, we do not mean compass indication, but true north as determined from the position of the polestar.

The most simple way to do this is to establish the position of the shadow of a vertical stick at the precise hour of true noon, making due allowance for the equation of time for the day. The amount to be added or subtracted at noon is given for each day of the year in large almanacs, such as *The World Almanac* published by the *New York World-Telegram*. The shadow line should be checked by observations on several days.

The time is read on a horizontal sundial at the place where the shadow of the point of the gnomon falls on the dial. Since the shadow rotates in an opposite direction from the apparent movement of the sun, it rotates counterclockwise.

The angle of the gnomon must be equal to the latitude of the place, and be positioned north and south. In a vertical sundial the angle will be 90° less the latitude.

On the following pages will be found four simple steps for laying out the dial. It would be best to make a dial first in wood, and check the accuracy by means of a watch before putting it into more substantial form.

The raised letters of the dial can be those used in sign-making, which can be purchased from most large art supply stores. The final dial can be made of a variety of materials. The least expensive would be to make a plaster cast from the wood model, which could later be pressed into a type of clay which hardens into a concretelike material. This is sold in art stores. A local iron foundry could

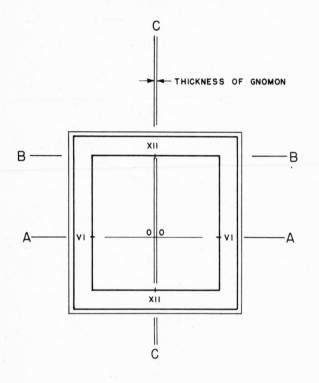

1. Draw the outline of the dial on paper larger than the dial. Draw line A-A slightly below center. Draw line B-B. Draw double line C-C at right angle to A-A in center of the dial. Space between the lines C-C should be equal to thickness of gnomon, since the shadow is cast by edges of gnomon. The VI-VI can now be marked at line A-A, the XII at lines C-C.

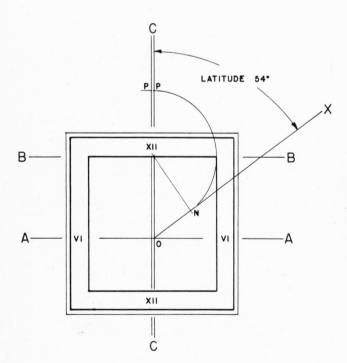

2. With a protractor draw line O-X at an angle to C-C equal in degrees to your latitude. (The latitude of the dial in this example is 54°.) Now draw line N-XII at right angle to line O-X. Now with a compass, establish the point P. The distance from XII-N is the same as XII-P.

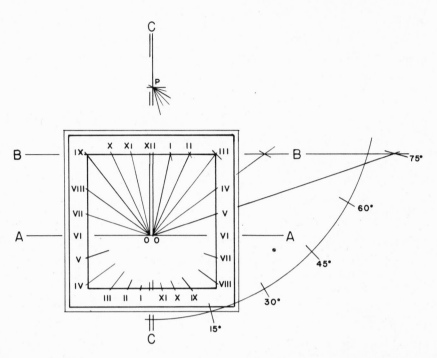

3. *With a protractor lay out a series of 15° angles from point P on line C-C. Indicate where each crosses line B-B by dots. Draw lines from these dots to point O. These lines establish the positions of hours I, II, III, IV, V. Repeat this operation on other side of dial, making allowance for thickness of gnomon. Projection of lines above VI gives hours below this line.*

4. *The base of the gnomon is equal to the distance O-XII on the dial. The angle N-O-XII to the base is that of the latitude where used, in this example, 54°.*

The gnomon is mounted at right angle to the base. The line O-XII must run north and south, with the figure XII north.

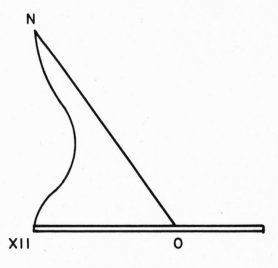

also duplicate it in cast iron with a sand mold. Some brass foundries produce castings in the same way.

The diagrams which are given show no ornamentation. A sundial lends itself to a variety of decorative treatments according to the taste and ability of the maker. Pressed wood ornamentation, such as is used on furniture, could be applied to a wood model easily. A local cabinet or furniture maker should know where these may be obtained.

To most of us, a sundial calls for a motto or inscription. Here are a few of many hundreds which have come down to us:

TEMPUS FUGIT
Time Flies

SIC TRANSIT GLORIA MUNDI
So Passes the Glory of the World

C'EST L'HEURE DE BIEN FAIRE
This Is the Hour To Do Good

COSI LA VITA
Such Is Life

I MARK ONLY THE SUNNY HOURS

IL EST PLUS TARD QUE VOUS CROYEZ
It Is Later Than You Think

THE HOUR PASSETH

TEMPUS AD LUCEM DUCIT VERITATEM
Time Brings Truth to Light

Time and Frequency Broadcasts

THE CORRECT TIME is regularly broadcast by radio stations in various parts of the world: the United States Naval Observatory from NSS, Annapolis, Maryland; NPG, Mare Island, California; NBA, Balboa, Canal Zone. The Dominion Observatory, Ottawa, Canada, broadcasts time signals continuously over station CHU, on frequencies of 3330, 7335, and 14670 kc. A similar service is provided by most of the larger nations.

The National Bureau of Standards of the United States Department of Commerce broadcasts six widely used technical services: standard radio frequencies, standard audio frequencies, standard time intervals, standard musical pitch, time signals, and radio propagation forecasts. The latter is used in radio communication. Radio stations are located in Beltsville, Maryland (WWV), and Hawaii (WWVA). Standard radio frequencies of 2.5, 5, 10, 15, 20, and 25 mc., accurate to 1 part in 100,000,000 as broadcast, are used by the communications and electronics industries.

The two standard audio frequencies of 440 and 600 cycles per second, which are broadcast at frequent intervals, permit accurate measurement or calibration of instruments operating in the audio or ultrasonic regions of the frequency spectrum.

The service also includes the broadcast of seconds pulses. These are broadcast for two minute, three minute, and five minute intervals between broadcasts of the audio frequencies. Each pulse has a duration of 0.005 second. The seconds pulses provide a useful standard time interval for quick and accurate measurement or calibration of time and frequency standards and timing devices.

The standard pitch for musical instruments in the United States has been based on a frequency of 440 cycles per second for note *A* above middle *C*, since 1925. The standard musical pitch of 440 cycles is broadcast 6 times per hour for a total of 18 minutes per hour. A simple short-wave radio receiver makes the musical pitch universally available. All instruments are made or tuned to this signal, and many piano tuners use it instead of a common tuning fork.

Time signals are broadcast in both code and voice. A schedule of the services and technical information is available from the National Bureau of Standards Boulder Laboratories, Boulder, Colorado.

Planetariums in the United States

VISITS TO THE PLANETARIUMS now found in many cities afford the interested lay-man an opportunity to view the movements of the stars, the planets, and various other celestial phenomena, and to better understand the relation between astronomy and time. The first planetarium in the United States was installed in the Adler Planetarium and Astronomical Museum in Chicago in 1930, and more than a million visitors viewed it yearly in its first three years. Others were later installed at the Franklin Institute in Philadelphia, the American Museum of Natural History in New York (the Hayden Planetarium), the Griffith Observatory in Los Angeles, the Peoples Observatory in Pittsburgh, and the University of North Carolina at Chapel Hill. All of these were equipped with the optical planetarium made by Carl Zeiss at Jena, Germany. The original Zeiss plant was a casualty of World War II, but has since been rebuilt and is once more making its precision projectors. American-made optical planetaria have been placed in the California Academy of Science in San Francisco, the Museum of Natural History at Springfield, Massachusetts, and elsewhere. The Spitz Laboratories of Philadelphia is one American firm making optical planetaria. The annual attendance at these various planetariums is probably greater than the total attendance at major baseball games, a fact of interest to those who feel that Americans lack an interest in culture.

Books for Further Reading

THE LITERATURE ON TIME, timepieces, and related subjects is perhaps the largest of any subject. Unfortunately, most of even relatively recent volumes are out-of-print, but some can usually be found in most libraries. Probably the largest American collection of books on time and astronomy is that in the United States Naval Observatory in Washington, D.C. A few volumes are noted below as a guide to a larger introduction to this vast subject, but is in no sense complete.

Brearley, Harry C. *Time Telling Through the Ages.* New York: Doubleday, Page & Company, 1919.
> Published for Robert H. Ingersoll & Brothers, it is particularly valuable for its information on the Ingersolls, and the contribution which they made to the expansion in the use of watches. Contains an excellent dictionary of horology.

Britten, Frederick J. *Old Clocks and Watches and Their Makers.* London: B. T. Batsford, 1922.
> Deals mostly with the historically important English clockmakers. Contains list of makers and dates.

Chamberlain, Paul M. *It's About Time.* New York: Richard R. Smith, 1941.
> A studious volume written by an engineer and amateur horologist. It presents a detailed study of the development of the escapement, with many scale drawings. Contains excellent biographies of important watch- and clockmakers.

Cuss, T. P. Camerer. *The Story of Watches.* London: Macgibbon & Kee, Ltd., 1952.
> The author, an English watchmaker, appraises the value of watch improvements with examples of watches from earliest times to today.

Duncan, John C. *Astronomy.* New York: Harper & Brothers, 1955.
> An easy to follow textbook on basic astronomy, with considerable information on the history and development of this important science with which time is so closely associated.

Fried, Henry B. *The Watch Repairers Manual.* New York: Van Nostrand Company, 1949.
> For the amateur who wishes to tinker with watches, or one who is learning the trade of watch repairing. More than four hundred line drawings to make each point clear, step by step.

———. *Bench Practices for Watch Repairers.* New York: Roberts Publishing Company, 1954.

A more advanced book on watch repairing, including chapters on parts making.

Gatty, H. K. F., and Eleanor Lloyd. *The Book of Sun Dials*. London: George Bell & Sons, 1889.

The most comprehensive book on the subject for the general reader, with hundreds of inscriptions and sketches of famous dials.

Humbert, B. *Swiss Self-Winding Watches*. Lausanne, Switzerland: Journal Suisse d'Horlogerie, 1956.

Detailed description with illustrations of the many types of Swiss self-winding watch mechanisms produced by the various makers. Of particular interest to the watch repairer.

Jaquet, Eugene, and Alfred Chapui. *La Montre Suisse de ses Origines à nos Jours*. Olten, Switzerland: Urs Graf-Verlag, 1945.

The most comprehensive story of watchmaking in Switzerland, with numerous fine plates in color and black and white of watches from earliest days to the present.

Milham, Willis I. *Time and Timekeepers*. New York: Macmillan Company, 1945.

A comprehensive semitechnical book on the history and development of clocks and watches up to the pocket watch.

Moldenke, Charles E. *The New York Obelisk*. Lancaster, Pennsylvania: Lancaster Press, 1935.

A highly interesting story of the obelisks and their inscriptions.

National Bureau of Standards. *Units and Systems of Weights and Measures,* Publication N.B.S. 570. Washington, D.C.: U. S. Government Printing Office, 1956.

Outlines the system of standards of time, length, mass (weight), and capacity, with comparative tables for the United States, England, and France.

Palmer, Brooks. *The Book of American Clocks*. New York: Macmillan Company, 1950.

A most complete presentation of American clockmakers and their work, with list of names and dates. Profusely illustrated.

Panth, Bhola D. *Consider the Calendar*. New York: Bureau of Publications, Teachers College, Columbia University, 1944.

A well-organized volume devoted to this single fascinating subject.

Rawlings, C. F. *The Science of Clocks and Watches*. New York: Pitman Publishing Company, 1948.

Outlines the basic mechanics of the components of clocks and watches, with mathematical formulas for gears, springs, escapements, etc.

Symonds, R. W. *Thomas Tompion, His Life and Work*. New York: B. T. Batsford, Ltd., 1951.

A beautifully illustrated volume, with many colored plates, and with the history of Tompion and other clockmakers of the period.

PERIODICALS

The American Horologist and Jeweler, Denver, Colorado, is the only American periodical devoted largely to watches and clocks. Their book department is probably the best for books on these subjects. There are two excellent Swiss journals with English editions: *La Suisse Horlogère,* La Chaux-de-Fonds, and *Journal Suisse d'Horlogerie,* Lausanne, Switzerland. In England there is *British Jeweller & Metalsworker.*

Index

Figures in italics indicate illustrations

PHOTO CREDITS

Page 51, Official United States Navy photo; page 57, Collection, Metropolitan Museum of Art; page 68, Royal Greenwich Observatory (copyright reserved); page 83, Collection, Metropolitan Museum of Art; page 87, Collection, Metropolitan Museum of Art; page 92 (left), Collection, Metropolitan Museum of Art; page 92 (right), Henry Fried Collection, photo by Irving Desfor; page 94, Collection, Metropolitan Museum of Art; page 95, Watchmakers of Switzerland, New York; page 109, Auguste Seiler Collection, photo by permission of Urs Graf Verlag, Basel, Switzerland; page 111, Collection, Metropolitan Museum of Art; page 116, Longines Watch Company; page 120, Longines Watch Company; page 121, Collection, Metropolitan Museum of Art; page 128, Longines Watch Company; page 134, Watchmakers of Switzerland, New York; page 138, National Bureau of Standards; page 139, Berg, Hedstrom & Company; page 148, National Bureau of Standards.

ABOUT THE AUTHOR

HARRISON J. COWAN was educated in the Boston public schools and Eric Pape School of Art. He worked briefly as a commercial artist, and later operated his own advertising agency for a number of years. During that time Mr. Cowan was particularly active in the production of radio programs. As principal speaker at the convention of the National Association of Broadcasters in 1929, he suggested a reorganization of the divisions of the radio industry, a plan which was soon adopted. He also produced the first commercial electrical transcription by the $33\frac{1}{3}$ r.p.m. system.

In 1938 he became associated with the Longines-Wittnauer Watch Company as Director of Public Relations, and in this capacity he actively participated in the well-known Longines Symphonette.

During his twenty-year association with Longines, Mr. Cowan has been an avid student of the subject of time. Since 1941 he has directed their sports timing activities. An expert in this field, he has organized the timing for sports events of all types, such as attempts on the water speed record and automobile speed trials on the Bonneville Salt Flats, Utah. Among other events were the United States Olympic Trials in 1948, 1952, and 1956, and the World Ski Championships at Rumford, Maine, and Aspen, Colorado, in 1950. He is presently organizing the complex system of electrical timing for the VIII Olympic Winter Games, which will be held at Squaw Valley, California, in February, 1960.

Mr. Cowan lives on a farm in Bucks County, Pennsylvania.

1 2 3 4 5 6 7 8 9 10 67 66 65 64 63 62 61 60 59 58